The Ultimate *Guided*

Relaxation

COLLECTION

Volume 1

meditations,
relaxations,
hypnotherapy scripts,
story metaphors

Edited by Tania Taylor

First published in 2022 by Fuzzy Flamingo
Copyright © Tania Taylor 2022

ISBN: 978-1-7397850-6-2

Editing and design by Fuzzy Flamingo
www.fuzzyflamingo.co.uk

A catalogue for this book is available from the British Library.

Laura, your words of wisdom inspire me every day to identify my dreams and make them happen now, not later. Forever in my thoughts and heart.

Acknowledgements

To everyone who has contributed to making this idea become a reality, from the authors to the copy writers and publishers, and to you the reader. Without all of you, this book would not be. A special thanks to Jen Parker from Fuzzy Flamingo Publishing, who has journeyed with me every step of the way. From the moment the idea came to mind, right through the maze of jigsaw fragments that ended with an elegantly and superbly produced finished masterpiece.

Contents

Introduction

Stories have been around since the beginning of time. To teach us lessons, to help us grow, to bring us hope, peace and calm, to help us learn and develop. Each story enabling us to create imagery inside our minds. In the beginning, perhaps we didn't realise the power of our imaginations. Or perhaps we did.

As the years have unfolded more and more research has been focused on the power of visualisation and the benefits to young and old alike. Studies have time and again demonstrated how powerful a short and simple relaxation can be, as well as the long-lasting benefits of regular exposure to more complex and lengthier guided relaxations and story metaphors.

Our busy lives and endless stressors result in lengthy periods of time where we as humans do not rest and relax. And yet we know how valuable resting, relaxing and taking care of our minds can be. We know doing this helps us cope better with the daily challenges life unexpectedly but continuously throws in our direction.

This book aims to use the power of relaxation and imagery to aid all those listening to the guided relaxations within, an opportunity to rest and relax. To recharge, unwind and unfold. Opportunities for peace and tranquillity. The ability to have confidence in oneself and to let go of unhelpful thoughts and behaviours. To connect with who they really are, instead of what the pressures of society say they should be. To be the version of themselves that follows their hopes and dreams, their desires, and aspirations. That version of themselves that has confidence in their abilities, who looks in the mirror and smiles with love, acceptance, and admiration. That person who faces life challenges with an inner strength they never knew existed, accessing inner resources they did not know were accessible to them until now. Creating the very best version of themselves so that they may go on to live a life with a certainty and secureness about who they are and a toolbox of resources that goes with them wherever they go. Helping them to succeed in achieving their goals and living life to the full, whatever that means to them.

Within this book, I hope that you *the reader* will find your practices are enhanced as you utilise the power within the written word to help create magnificent journeys that can take your guests from natural woodland glades, to far away galaxies, from calming chakra balancing, through to snowy villages. Each guided relaxation creating feelings of calm and stillness. With lessons about loving oneself and coping with overwhelm, to hypnobirthing and even past life work.

This carefully selected collection of relaxations aims to aid your professional practice with the people you work with, whether you are using them in one to one or group settings. My hope in creating *The Ultimate Guided Relaxations Collection* is to enable you as *the reader* the ability to utilise the power of the imagination to enhance the lives of those you work with. The more this beautiful and natural way of healing our minds and bodies is used across the globe, the calmer and healthier we can all be.

How to get the best out of delivering relaxations, meditations, and hypnotherapy sessions to your listeners:

When using relaxations such as those found within this book, there are a few tips that can help you to enhance the experience for your listener.

Your opening words – During the sessions I deliver face to face – in group and one-to-one settings – I will often begin with the following:

> *"Just focusing on your breathing for me now, not changing the breath, just being aware of the breath in and the breath out. Perhaps paying attention to the journey of the breath as it enters through your nostrils or lips and touches the back of your throat. Noticing the impact on your chest, lungs, and stomach muscles as you inhale and exhale."*

This gives me some time to check I have everything in front of me that I need, and to readjust my own seating position to ensure I will be comfortable throughout.

Next, I will say something along the lines of:

"During this session you may hear noises inside the room, or outside of the room, but they are of no concern to you now. If you find your mind noticing any noise, allow yourself to acknowledge it, and then simply let it go by bringing your focus and attention back to the sound of my voice."

For work with online listeners I may amend this slightly to include:

" … outside of the room, if it is not for your benefit, it is of no concern to you now … " and I will also add *"please ensure that you and those surrounding you will not come to any harm should you fall asleep during this relaxation, this means ensuring you are lying comfortably, candles are not lit, and you are not listening whilst driving or bathing".*

And then I will begin.

Transitioning from one type of relaxation to another – If we are mixing and matching our relaxations, sometimes they don't always flow from one to the other. I find using a filler line such as *"and whilst you are feeling so relaxed, you find somewhere comfortable to lie back, close your eyes and fall into a deep and relaxing sleep. And as you sleep you have a dream. You dream of … "* You can replace this sentence with all kinds of similar alternatives. From lying in a hammock, to sitting down on a bench. From saying the listener is having a dream, to telling the listener that they find themselves listening to a story. It is up to you as the professional to decide what will work most effectively for you, your listeners, and the scripts you are pooling together.

The environment – Aim for a relaxing and quiet environment. If this is not possible, it is advisable to begin your session by stating something like *"During this session you may hear noises inside the room, you may hear noises outside of the room, but these are of no concern to you now. Give yourself permission to acknowledge a noise should you notice it at all, and then let it go by bringing your focus and attention back to the sound of my voice."*

Your voice – If you are new to the world of guided relaxations then I would highly recommend recording yourself reading a relaxation and listening to it back. For some people this may feel initially like a form of torture! But the more you listen to your own voice, the more you can accept that your voice is a beautiful one. And when you have belief in yourself, others will have even more belief in you and the words you are gifting to them during a relaxation session.

The other benefit of listening to your own recording is being able to acknowledge room for improvement and ways you would like to see yourself improve. Try listening to other people delivering similar relaxation sessions. What do you like about their tone, their pauses, the way they take a breath, the inflections they use, the flow of their words. Practicing with listeners you are familiar with first can help, although is not necessary.

Your personal touch – Rarely do I read a script word for word. Relaxation scripts are incredible for giving you an aim and purpose for your session, but often they will use language that doesn't come natural to you. I remember one of the first scripts I was ever given during training used the word "Zephyr." I replaced it with "a gentle breeze" as it wasn't a word I would ever find myself using. Don't be afraid to write on your scripts, crossing out and replacing words that are more suited to you and your personality. All my scripts are full of scribbles.

As your confidence grows you will also find yourself ad-libbing more frequently based on what the listener/s have said to you before you began your session. Thus, creating a more personalised and meaningful relaxation for the individuals you are working with. For example, a script may suggest the listener will find inner strength such as confidence and determination. But during the session they may have told you they want more self-belief and courage, so you might find yourself replacing the descriptive words to benefit your listener.

Help and support:

If you find yourself with any questions about how best to deliver the scripts you would be welcome to post these in my Facebook group for therapists at www.facebook.com/groups/TaniaTaylor and if you would like to see how I deliver relaxations online with groups of people you are welcome to join my Calm Your Mind Facebook group at www.facebook.com/groups/CalmYourMindFree.

How to use this book

This book contains so many elements that can be used individually as short, light meditations, or together as deeper, more complex relaxations. This chapter aims to give you guidance on the diverse types of relaxations within this book and how you can mix and match to create lighter or deeper, longer or shorter sessions dependent on your needs as a professional and your aims for the people you are working with.

Throughout this book you will find a handy key to the different ingredients found in each individual relaxation you are reading. Below are the descriptions of each and how you may find mixing and matching them to be useful for you and your listeners.

Breathing Techniques

Breathing techniques are a great resource for the people you work with in managing stress and overwhelming situations. They are often fairly short and can be used alone or as a prelude to a progressive muscle relaxation or meditation.

Progressive Muscle Relaxation

Progressive Muscle Relaxations (PMR) use guided instruction from the reader to assist the person listening in relaxing all the muscles in their body. Sometimes they can use very direct language, such as "relaxing all the muscles in your hands." Others may use guided imagery to help aid the relaxation of all the muscles such as "feeling the oceans waves wash over and through your whole body relaxing and calming you."

Using PMR is a great prelude to a story metaphor, meditation, or deepener. It enables the listeners to get into a relaxed and comfortable state of mind and body ready for what is to come next. You can also use PMR on its own if your aim is to simply help the listener to have a few moments to relax. Throughout this book you will find PMR's of varying lengths. I suggest choosing these as a helpful addition to your session depending on the time you have allocated for the relaxation.

Deepeners and Inductions

Deepeners and inductions are more commonly used in hypnotherapy, although over the years you find them appearing within some of the longer meditation scripts.

The aim of a deepener is to take the person listening into an even deeper state of relaxation after using a PMR. This deep state of relaxation often enables the conscious mind to switch off and relax and creates a more active subconscious mind that is further open to suggestions found in the meditation or story metaphor. Suggestions used will always be accepted if they are meaningful to the client and for their benefit. If the listener does not accept or agree with a suggestion, then they will simply come out of the trance state. It is important that you notify your listeners of this before making suggestions when they are in such a deeply submerged state of mind.

A deepener or induction usually includes some kind of sequencing, such as counting down steps or moving downwards or upwards in some way. There are also confusional inductions which work on creating a confusing sequence that the listener tries to follow but eventually lets go of and submits to complete relaxation. Confusional deepeners are best used for listeners who may be struggling to relax and let go of tension.

Deepeners and inductions should be placed before a story metaphor, guided imagery, or meditation.

Story Metaphors

Story metaphors are beautiful stories of varying lengths that serve to have our listeners' minds noticing parallels between the story and their own lives.

The aim of story metaphors is to aid our listeners in finding a solution to their difficulties themselves from listening to the story. Story metaphors can often be found in meditative and hypnotic scripts and guided relaxations. They contain confidence boosters and life lessons that only serve to benefit the listener. They rarely contain relaxation tools and so you will often use these at the end of a grouping. For example, you might choose to use a breathing technique, PMR, and then story metaphor. Or a PMR, Deepener, and finish with a story metaphor.

Meditation

A meditation uses guided imagery to promote self-reflection or musings. It can be in the form of a story metaphor and can also use breathing techniques and PMR. It rarely uses deepeners unless the professional wishes to extend the length of the relaxation or assist the listener in achieving a deeper state of relaxation.

Meditations can be used individually but can also be mixed and matched with all the above.

About the authors

Anne Gregory

Anne is a solution focused clinical hypnotherapist and psychotherapist who's been helping people change their lives for the better since 2013.

She's enjoyed writing since the age of 12, having had a wonderfully encouraging English teacher at school. Being part of this book is a lifelong dream come true.

Language is such a powerful tool and the language patterns Anne has created are designed to engage both the conscious and subconscious mind for maximum effect.

Anne is available for bookings on yoga retreats and can be commissioned to create specific language patterns for you.

www.annegregoryhypnotherapy.com
www.facebook.com/annegregoryhypnotherapy

Caroline Measures

Caroline Measures is a Women's Coach and Therapist. She uses a blend of techniques to reduce anxiety, boost well-being and help women break free from the past so they can step into a life they love. Working with groups, one-to-one, and through online courses, Caroline uses hypnosis, NLP, mindfulness, flower essences and many other tools to bring about positive transformations. She is also a published writer and speaker and can provide scripts and recordings, as well as leading retreats or collaborating on events. Contact hello@carolinemeasures.com or visit www.carolinemeasures.com

Clare Murchison

Clare is an intuitive practitioner using hypnosis, psychotherapy, HeartHealing™, coaching and NLP, enabling women to free themselves from unhelpful beliefs, unwanted patterns of behaviour and thinking and childhood wounds that are blocking them from receiving.

She runs her own practice, supporting one-to-one clients and offering group programmes, which empower women to be the best version of themselves with renewed confidence and inner belief, lighter, brighter and more empowered.

A competent and engaging speaker both in person and online, she inspires others to reconnect with who they truly are and believe change is possible.

https://www.clareatrefreshingminds.co.uk/
https://www.facebook.com/clareatrefreshingminds

Diane Jennings

Diane Jennings is a solution focused hypnotherapist working with children, young people and adults who experience anxiety and other related issues. She is passionate about supporting people to work towards their preferred future and has been writing language patterns for the last four years. She loves writing and the escapism it brings. She has spent over twenty years working in the NHS as a paediatric nurse and is a wife and mum to three fantastic children. Her motto in life is 'I can, I will'.

www.dianejennings.life
https://www.facebook.com/dianejenningssolutionfocusedhypnotherapy/

Elaine Neale

Elaine is a clinical hypnotherapist and psychotherapist specialising in solution focused hypnotherapy. Based in Central Scotland and online, Elaine combines running her successful practice with writing and training the hypnotherapists of the future as an assistant lecturer with the nationally recognised Clifton Practice (CPHT) in Edinburgh.

If you have enjoyed Elaine's work and are interested in more, why not consider booking her to speak to your group, write a relaxation or language pattern specifically for your use with clients, classes or groups, collaborate on a project, or join your retreat.

Contact Elaine at Elaine.Neale@Happy-Hypnotherapy.co.uk or find out more at www.happy-hypnotherapy.co.uk/corporate

Emma Last

Emma has over twenty years' experience in senior leadership, change making and performance. She founded Progressive-Minds in 2018, after becoming severely burnt out herself, when she had her own 'Human Reboot'. Emma is a speaker, trainer and coach for individuals and workplaces who want to increase their well-being, resilience and performance. She has co-written the First Aid Industry Body's accredited training *Workplace Mental Health and Well-being* for those working with Children and Young People. Her podcast 'Human Reboot' got to number 22 in Mental Health Awareness week in 2021 and she is an Amazon number one best-selling author.

www.thehumanrebootmovement.com
https://progressive-minds.co.uk

Jane Hill

Jane is a modern mystic living in rural Scotland. She makes meditative journeys into the sacred Otherworld and works with guided meditation to help others to connect to their true, loving, compassionate, wise, healing and healed heart.

You can find out more about her and her work at:
www.amethystliving.co.uk
and her Facebook group: The Secret Meditation Garden.

Jeff Lloyd

Jeff is the author of *The Sat Nav Guide to Your Soul* and *Wherever You Are You Are Here*. Jeff practises Hypnotherapy, Past Life Regression, Spiritual Release Therapy and EFT (Emotional Freedom Technique). Jeff has over twenty years' experience, treating clients, holding workshops and public speaking. Jeff now lives in the Northwest of England working from the Wigan and Southport areas.

www.jefflloyd.co.uk and Positive Change/facebook

Karina Price

Karina is a multi-award-winning hypnotherapist based in Exeter, Devon, and is a writer and narrator on the Sleepiest App. She specialises in anxiety and runs weekly group relaxation classes. Passionate about yoga, Karina fully appreciates the healing effect of the mind body connection, which underpins her work as a hypnotherapist.

Karina also facilities well-being talks on stress and anxiety and provides relaxation classes at business events and retreats. Karina can be commissioned to write scripts and can be booked for wellness retreats and corporate events.

Website: www.karinapricehypnotherapy.co.uk
Instagram: Karina Price Hypnotherapy

Kathleen Bradley

A hypnotherapist and emotional freedom technique (EFT) practitioner, Kathleen has always found pleasure in helping others overcome their obstacles and challenges. She started working with vulnerable women both in refugee and helpline roles.

More recently this has been through practising hypnotherapy and EFT. Both holistic approaches are talking therapies that involve building a trusted connection with clients.

Like many, her discovery of these started through self-help following a serious illness. She turned to books and later trained and qualified to practice.

Maggie Matthews

Maggie is a qualified Hypnotherapist, Bereavement and Grief Counsellor and Angelic Reiki Healer.

She is available to do one-to-one sessions or group sessions for meditation, relaxation and healing. She is an inspirational, motivational speaker and writes scripts for personal and professional individuals or groups with specific requirements.

Hypnotherapy, Counselling and Healing have had a positive impact on her life and have brought her to a place of peace, love and happiness. She wants to be able to support and guide others to have the life they want, to be empowered and in a place of love, light and healing.

You can contact Maggie via her website: www.maggiematthewsauthor.com

Norah Mahony

Norah is a worldwide hypnotherapist and soul-led success coach, supporting her clients to design and reach their goals in life.

Norah combines life and business coaching, hypnotherapy and other healing modalities so that her clients can connect with what they truly want from life, design their goals, take inspired action and finally see the results that they desire, by moving through the blocks and limiting beliefs that have previously held them back. Norah has an ongoing passion towards personal and professional development, to coach people to connect with themselves at soul level, in alignment and joy.

https://www.facebook.com/norah.josephine.5

www.norahginty.com

Pamela Gilvear

Pamela is an experienced Psychotherapist, Empowerment Coach and Usui Reiki Teacher based in Gloucestershire, England. She works in her private practice, offering 1:1 sessions, workshops, events speaking and bespoke relaxation script writing.

Her passion is supporting others in discovering their own pace, finding the right relaxation resources for them, in order to live a life that feels balanced and aligned to their soul's purpose.

If you are looking to have a bespoke relaxation script written or a speaker at your event/group, she would welcome your enquiry to discuss your requirements further. You can contact her at:

Website: www.lighthouse-therapies.co.uk

Email: pamela@lighthouse-therapies.co.uk

Paula Greensted

With a background in business development and marketing, Paula decided on a change of career after discovering the positive effects of hypnotherapy on her own health and well-being. She trained as a solution focused clinical hypnotherapist and now runs her own practice, Inner Spark Hypnotherapy, helping clients to flourish and thrive in life.

Paula is also a prize-winning story writer and enjoys combining her twin passions of writing and psychology to produce creative pieces for use in her hypnotherapy practice and other commissions.

Paula can be contacted by email at info@innersparkhypnotherapy.co.uk on Facebook at www.facebook.com/innersparkhypnotherapy or LinkedIn.

Sarah Bamber

Sarah is a human Massage & Holistic Therapist; an Equine Sports Therapist, and a Mindful Walking Guide – leading people to finding their true selves in nature. Sarah lives offgrid in the Pennines with her family and animals, she loves the outdoors and finds peace and inspiration in the hills with her horses and dogs.

She holds weekly relaxation sessions in her Facebook group 'Being you in Body & Mind'. You are most welcome to join here https://www.facebook.com/groups/777184616207013

Mindfulness and yoga have been part of her life for over 26 years, and have helped immensely with anxiety, severe pain and stress.

Sarah is available for relaxation days/weekends & retreats. Her website is https://www.sarah-bamber.co.uk

Tania Taylor

Tania is an international multi-award-winning hypnotherapist, psychotherapist and mentor. She provides 1:1 support face to face and via video link worldwide, supporting people using solution focused brief therapy. Alongside this role, Tania is a lecturer at multiple worldwide training schools for therapists and a #1 best-selling author of several books. Tania is regularly commissioned to attend retreats and write tailored relaxation scripts for specific settings. For more information or to commission Tania for your business, you can reach her at www.Tania-Taylor.co.uk or you can join her free relaxation group www.facebook.com/CalmYourMindFree

CHAPTER ONE

Acceptance and self-belief

Blue tide

A metaphor for self-acceptance /
overcoming mistakes

Karina Price

Once there was a woman who lived out at sea. She spent day after day sailing the sea alone, watching all the other boats go on their merry way. Their boats were big and shiny. They were strong, and all these boats seemed to know where they were heading. They went with speed and direction.

This woman was sad and lonely, and her boat was old. And she spent most of her time not sailing in a particular direction but trying to stop her boat from sinking. She was tired, she was desolate. And she was just about keeping her head above water.

One day, she reflected on why she was sailing an old boat with no sense of direction, and why it was so unfair that everybody else just seemed to know where they were heading; they looked forward to the adventures before them, having fun and full of joy and optimism.

She wondered whether it was because she had made mistakes on her journey. Perhaps she had taken the wrong path and made the wrong decisions. And maybe it was her mistakes that led her into this bleak area of the sea.

One day, there was a huge storm, the biggest storm that she'd ever seen; it came unexpectedly. All the other people in the big, strong boats struggled to battle the storm and it consumed them. But the sea woman was resilient, she knew how to overcome the storm for she had experienced rough waters many times. And, after the storm had gone, she awoke on a beautiful beach.

A beach that she had never seen before. A beach that felt like home. She was no longer keeping her head above water. And, on this island, she came across treasure ... the treasure of realising her inner strengths.

Footprints in the sand

A guided relaxation, visualising the enjoyment and freedom
of a quiet walk on the beach

Elaine Neale

You are standing on the beach … an expanse of shoreline stretching away either side of you. At the moment the beach is a narrow strip of sand, but ever growing as the tide recedes … Behind you, dunes sprout tufts of hardy, blue-green grass amongst the soft sand that the sea never reaches. The yielding sand down to the tide line is dimpled with old footprints of others who have been down to enjoy the shore. The wind off the sea has softened their outlines, leaving them undulating trails like indistinct waves.

The receding tide leaves a band of firm, wet sand … darker and easier to walk on … but for now you're content to be still … watching the waves rising out to sea, and breaking as they draw closer to the shore until their foamy edges run up the sand in numerous small fans of bubbly white, and sigh gently against the sand in a soft exhale …

The waves are beautiful … sparkling and making the daylight dance. They sound so peaceful as they rhythmically pull in and out. You watch them for a while as your heartbeat and breath comfortably slow … as though matching the natural cadence of the waves. You can feel the breeze and fine salty spray on your skin … you're part of the scene … like you belong in this place … belong to the beach.

Looking around, you choose a direction and set out, walking slowly along the firm sand. With every step you take, water seeps up from the sand, oozing around your feet before draining away as you leave your footprint behind. Every now and again a wave bubbles over your feet as you walk, and you feel the sand suck away beneath you slightly. It tickles pleasantly but doesn't impede you. The water is cool … refreshing but not too cold … and you don't mind getting wet.

The newly exposed sand is dotted with small stones … shells … and the natural flotsam left behind by the escaping tide. As you relax and let your mind drift, you can see that they form interesting patterns around you, … drawing your attention … … As you walk along, you come across the perfect stick for drawing with … sturdy and just the right length. Brushing a few grains of sand from it, you start to draw in the sand. Perhaps you draw patterns or join the dots between the shells and stones to form pictures … or just squiggle random lines. Maybe you'll write your name instead. Whatever you choose to draw today is made special by its impermanence … destined to be transient and reclaimed by the sea in a few short hours and be delivered anew as a blank canvas.

As you look behind, back the way you came, you see the lines you have traced … and your own footsteps meandering alongside, around and through them … adding to the intricacy of the pattern. A little of yourself written into the beach, showing you were there. Up ahead the sand remains pristine … ready for you to make your mark. Try something new or revisit something familiar. It's laid out before you like a world of possibilities … waiting expectantly for someone to come along … someone like you. What will you do with that potential? That ever-increasing expanse of sand? What would you like to do … ?

Perhaps you want to cut loose and joyfully run or dance along it for a stretch … no one's watching … you can do that if you want to … and it really wouldn't matter if someone were to see you … share your natural joy and exuberance with them … make them smile too! Maybe you'd like to run into the sea … playing with the waves, kicking up the water and splashing it into the air … You might like to build a sandcastle, maybe one with a moat for the seawater to fill … or bury your feet in the sand and enjoy the sensation of its weight enclosing them …

Take a few moments now and imagine yourself doing just what you want to do … … it may be one of these things … or something completely different … … something that you enjoy … that brings you happiness … and peace … …

As you make your way further along the beach, the sand becomes dotted with patches of rock ... home to rock pools left behind by the careless sea, teeming with life. Crabs and small fish dart about, seaweed floating in the small eddies they create ... a miniature world awaiting the tide's return to change it again and make it new.

Stepping up and over the rocks, you head back up the beach, away from the water and onto the soft, warm sand. Its warmth is appreciated after the cool water ... There's a large and welcoming boulder ahead, smooth and ageless ... a perfect place to rest for a while and contemplate all that you've seen and done on your journey along the shore ... maybe even what you're going to do on your return journey ... or just to allow this lovely feeling to embrace you ... The rock is holding the warmth of the day, encouraging you to sit down ... you stretch out your back and limbs against the reassuring solidity of the boulder ... absorb the stored warmth into your body ... and just ... relax.

Healing light of self-love

Heal trauma and grief of the past

Maggie Matthews

I would like you to take a nice deep breath in and let it out slowly, allowing your eyes to close … let your body relax. Breathe in and out … feel the tensions starting to ease from your body. Take another deep breath in and let it out slowly because, at this moment in time, you haven't a care in the world, nobody wanting anything, nobody needs anything, this is your time for you to relax, to let go and enjoy.

I would like you to imagine a pure white light coming down from the universe into the top of your head, down through your shoulders, all the way into your heart space … opening your heart, filling it with love, releasing all of the hurt, pain, grief that you have suffered in the past … the white light makes you feel weightless, as if you are floating on air … all of your worries and life burdens have been dissolved and disappeared … you feel immense love and it is pouring out of your heart, down through the rest of your body, entering every cell, every muscle and nerve ending, lighting it up in pure love and releasing all the negativity that has been held there for so long.

You feel an overwhelming sense of happiness, peace and joy … a new sense of freedom … new love and respect for yourself … for you are worthy and you are enough. You are beautiful on the inside and on the outside and everyone that meets you feels the love that radiates from you … the self-love that you deserve, that you are worthy of. Just listen to the inner voice that softly tells you to forgive yourself for being so hard on yourself … for you are deserving of all the love that the universe has to offer … be open to receive the love, so that you can love in return ... love yourself, for you are pure love ... you are special ... you are kind and you are sensitive ... you are caring and you are peaceful ... you are happy ... you are everything that you need to be ... you are well deserving of the love that you desire ... you are perfect in every way ... you are amazing and you are worthy of everything that the universe has to offer to you today and every day.

Be open to receive what is rightfully yours ... to forgive and let go of what no longer serves you. Be kind to yourself and let go of the past and the present ... be happy at this moment, for this moment is your life. Let the light shine warmly inside you and be that light that shines out of you. You have the power of love to forgive yourself and be you, for that is all you need to do. Be unique, be deserving and love yourself as you would anyone else. Nurture yourself and have a heart full of love. Be an inspiration to others to show them how to love themselves ... just like you love yourself. Have gratitude now for this healing white light that fills you with joy, peace, love and contentment ... for you are now surrounded by love and filled with love for yourself and others.

It is time now ... to slowly come back to the present ... from a place of light, love and healing.

Let your dreams be your wings

A metaphor to help create self-belief

Karina Price

There was a young woman who loved to go to bed each night, as this meant she could escape the reality of her everyday life. Every night she would dream that she could fly, and she would fly to different parts of the world taking in the beauty of people and places.

Flying gave her the confidence to do the things that she truly wanted to, as she knew if she messed up or something went wrong, she could fly away from her problems and nobody would judge her; this ability to fly away helped her to feel safe.

She dreamt of pursing the job of her dreams, freeing herself from old unhelpful thoughts and behaviours and having the courage to break away from toxic relationships and speaking her truth to the people she loved.

One night she dreamt that she flew to a deserted tropical island and settled down onto the beach. She started to draw patterns in the sand with a broken bamboo stick, whilst gazing up at the stars and noticing how they shine so bright. Whilst playing with the sand she discovered a glass bottle, which contained a stained piece of paper imprinted with a message. It read "all our dreams come true if we have the courage to pursue them, now with the stick you have chosen it is time to write them". As she looked up everything was yellow, as though covered by star dust. In this moment she started to write her dreams in the sand ...

"I am happy"

"I make my own choices that feel right for me"

"I trust the process and I follow my intuition"

"I enjoy trying new things and stepping outside of my comfort zone"

"I choose to spend time with people that inspire me and make me smile"

"I believe in me"

"I have the courage to challenge my limits"

The next morning, she woke up feeling different. She realised that whatever the mind can conceive and believe it can achieve and that everything around her … her house, car, clothes, furniture all started in the imagination of someone … someone who had the self-belief to make their dreams come true. She decided that instead of relying on her dreams at night to be a place to escape, she would let her dreams be her wings in her waking day.

The allotment

A metaphor to help change your perspective/
overcome negative thinking

Karina Price

One day a wonderful opportunity arose in the small village of Becksville, when a farmer donated some of his land so that the villagers could grow their own fruit and vegetables.

One woman was filled with excitement and joy as she made her way to the allotment. As she sowed the seeds she sang and danced and every day she would tend to her land with tenderness and care. Her fruits soon started to grow – sweet strawberries and berries and colourful spring vegetables. She was delighted that her efforts had paid off and this filled her with happiness.

But her neighbours patch looked bare … nothing to see apart from dry, hard land full of weeds and hurtful thorns. The woman was angry and resentful towards her neighbour, thinking that surely her land was more fortuitous than hers … she focused on the thorns and her anger grew.

One day her rage overcame her, and she confronted her neighbour … "this is your fault, my land is barren because you chose the rich soil, my land isn't good enough and now I have given up tending to it".

And her neighbour replied "We are both blessed with the same rich soil … I tend to my land every day … I see the crops in my mind's eye and feel their beauty before it arrives … "

And she went on to tell her angry neighbour … "you tend to your land every day … you see the thorns and feel the disappointment before it arrives … "

The angry neighbour contemplated her neighbour's wise words ... she realised that all this time she had focused on lack, and this fuelled the weeds ... from that moment on she focused on the outcome she wanted ... very soon the barren land was no more ... she smiled as she sang and danced and tended to her crops ... she realised that what we focus on we attract and this wonderful realisation changed her entire life ... we must believe it before we see it.

The little snowflake

Recognition of our resilience through life's many changes and celebrating the uniqueness that is you

Clare Murchison

The little snowflake was falling softly, gracefully through the atmosphere. It was not alone. Millions and millions of snowflakes were drifting down, as though in a magical dance choreographed by an invisible force, each one playing its part whilst on its own path, tumbling, swirling towards the planet below. Moving together in harmony, each in its own space, instinctively knowing the role it was here to play. Trusting that it was doing its very best and nothing else was required.

Slowly floating through the dark night sky, the little snowflake had time to consider the journey it had taken to be here right now, in this moment, filling the void of night with icy beauty.

It remembered waiting for the rays of springtime sun to cast light on to the frozen landscape, freeing it from where it rested. And the sun came. The warmth gave the frozen droplet the power to change to liquid, so once again it was free to move. And it did. Grasping the opportunities, finding its way, trusting it was going to go well.

As the little snowflake makes its way towards earth, it sees the rivers it had flowed within, enabling him to make his way across the land so very easily. He had travelled with hope and excitement alongside so many other water droplets. Part of the network of nature as they navigated their way towards warmer climates, noticing the changing colours of nature, the different sounds. Enjoying feeling connected. Sensing he was part of something bigger than he could comprehend. Trusting each move was the right one as he looked forward confidently with anticipation to what was to come. More opportunities, more special moments, more adventures.

Looking down, the little snowflake saw the hills, the valleys, the lakes with a different perspective, understanding more and more about how it all connected and appreciating how magical life on earth truly was. He thought of the words he had heard, the lives he had touched, where he had brought hope or life or beauty, and he felt proud of what he had accomplished.

The little snowflake knew he was absolutely unique. No other snowflake was quite like him. He was one of a kind, an individual, formed by his experiences, his journey and that meant that he was truly special.

Yet he loved being part of this snowfall, of being connected with other like creations, whilst swirling and twirling in his own beautiful and unique way down towards the surface of the earth. And, as the snowflakes neared their destination, they collectively coated the world in frosty white.

He rests, surrounded by hundreds of thousands of other flakes of crisp icy white snow, hearing the laughter of children – their excitement; their joy; their playfulness. He can sense their anticipation of fun as they see the snowy playground freshly created.

The little snowflake knew his role had altered as he travelled to this moment. His purpose had changed. Once here to give life to plants, crops and animals or to sparkle in fast-flowing rivers or generate energy as he rushed down a waterfall, he realised his purpose now was bringing happiness and beauty to the earth no matter how fleetingly.

In all his delicate and translucent beauty, he plays his part in decorating the world as a winter wonderland, forming a snowball and then a snowman. The little snowflake knows he will soon thaw and once again have the opportunity to travel to the earth as a water droplet, taking each day as it comes and knowing how exciting it will be.

CHAPTER TWO

Changing perspective

A December miracle

Story metaphor for people struggling with stress and overwhelm at Christmas

Tania Taylor

There was a very busy woman. So busy, in fact, she rarely had time to do anything for herself. She worked a busy job, she helped take care of others when she wasn't working, and often worked more hours so she could reach her deadlines.

Every year, although she heard talk of Christmas, it didn't really feel like the festive season had arrived. She couldn't quite put her finger on why, but it seemed like the festive season – the smiles, the joy, the love – was happening to others and not to herself. So, every year she carried on working, and taking care of others, feeling more and more disconnected.

Then one crisp, early December morning, she arrived in the office and checked her pigeonhole and there was a beautiful, elegant envelope with a ruby red wax seal. She placed it gently on her desk and looked at it for a few moments, paying attention to the embossed, thick cream paper, and the stamp within the wax. When she thought no one was looking, she opened it up and there inside was a ticket.

Not just any ticket, this ticket was for a few days away in a log cabin just for her. She smiled at the gesture, and quickly tucked the envelope away, acknowledging that she just didn't have the time to go away right now. It was December after all, deadlines were looming, deadlines for work projects, deadlines for buying gifts for people. She just didn't have the time.

Later that day, she was called in to see the manager. Her first thought was that she must have made some terrible mistake. Tentatively walking into the office, a stomach full of nerves, she waited to find out if she was going to be disciplined. Instead, and to her utter surprise, she was asked what time she was leaving today to go on her trip.

Flabbergasted, she said she couldn't. She didn't have the time. Her manager told her she must make the time and she must leave at once. Now, her manager was a very persuasive person, so off she went, with a new goal for the next few days. She was to rest, revive and enjoy the festivities. How this was going to be possible when she felt so detached, she had no idea. But she gathered all she needed and set off, following her sat nav to her unknown destination.

The drive was a difficult one, winding roads and hills, but eventually she arrived at her destination. It had already had snow here and her cabin was surrounded with the inconvenient white stuff. The evergreen tree stood tall outside, full of snow and, although she felt it should look picturesque, instead she felt everything looked dull. She took her bags from the car parking space, down some wooden steps that led directly to the cabin.

With each step down, she saw herself getting closer and closer to a place of calm. A place where nothing else and no one else mattered. A place where she could 'just be'. And, as she walked down those steps, she could feel a strange transformation taking place within her. Her breathing, despite the crisp, cold air and carrying her bags, was slowing. Her shoulders that had held so much tension unknowingly for so long were relaxing. And, with each step down, she felt more and more like her old self was returning.

How had she lost her old self, she pondered. But it didn't matter. For all that mattered was that she was beginning to feel more like her old self than she had known in a long time, and it felt good. By the time she reached the bottom of the steps, she was smiling. And, as she looked around at her surroundings, everything appeared so much brighter, and lighter, so much more colourful. It was as if she had been walking round with dark sunglasses on for so long that she hadn't noticed what life could look like if she had taken them off.

With a new sense of curiosity, she opened the cabin door and was hit by a wave of subtle warmth. She stamped the snow from her feet and removed her coat, walking from room to room in awe of this magical place. She could swear she even saw a sparkle as she looked at a painting of Santa Claus hung in the hallway. His cheeks were rosy, his belly round, his button lips were smiling, and she felt comforted somehow.

After unpacking and making herself at home, for she now felt it really was homely and comforting, she decided she would take a walk to the local village. The sun was low in the sky as dusk approached and there was a well-lit path that led the short walk to the village.

And for the first time in a long time, she walked with her head held high and a smile on her face. The dark sunglasses were off, and she could see everything so much clearer. Now she could notice the dogs that were wrapped up in Christmas jumpers as they walked, she noticed a window display depicting kindness and gratitude, the Christmas lights shining brightly from the lantern street lamps. And, as she was feeling brave, she took a moment to turn around and around on the spot and absorb the magical surroundings.

There were the carol singers and their merry audience, the people bustling and talking joyfully, the shop keepers taking pride in their businesses. As she spun, it began to rain. In times past, she knew she would have cursed and got mad, but now she allowed herself to notice the rain, to dance in the rain and splash in the puddles just like the children were.

Her old self really had returned. Everything was different, and yet everything remained exactly the same. And all she had to do was to take a moment to 'just be'. To take a breather from being busy. To take off the dark glasses and look around the world with curiosity instead of ignorance.

And every festive period from there on in, she was reminded to spend time on herself. She was reminded that taking a moment to turn around and absorb all of her surroundings was something valuable to her. And each time she did, she felt herself reconnect with the feelings of love, gratitude and giving at Christmas, and to reconnect with that version of herself she knows and loves.

Bypassing your conscious mind

A confusional induction for people who struggle to relax

Jeff Lloyd

Now that you're comfortable, I want you to pick a spot in front of you on the wall or ceiling and focus only on that spot, really focus on and zoom into that spot with your eyes and, as you do so, you may feel your eyes want to blink. That's fine, just keep focused on that point and, as your eyes continue to blink, just allow yourself to relax even more. Take this moment to focus upon yourself, this is your time, a special moment of time out of your busy day, just for you to relax and let go of all your cares and worries ... and, as you begin to let go and relax now even more, just allow your eyes to gently close; that's right, really relax those eyelids, just let them melt and stick together. Relax them so much until you feel unable to open them and, as you do so, let all the muscles around your eyes relax and all the muscles on your face, the muscles around your mouth, your nose and your cheeks ... that's right, just let them all relax. Focus now on your forehead; that's where we keep a lot of tension and all our thoughts and all our worries, so just let those muscles relax as well and allow those thoughts and worries just to drift away. As you do so, let that relaxation run down your face, down your neck and your throat, all the way down to your shoulders, really relax them now because it's here on our shoulders we can carry the weight of the world and all our troubles, so just let those shoulders relax completely. As they continue to relax, just allow that relaxation to run down your left arm, all the way down to your hand and the tips of your fingers and, as you do so, you may find your right arm feels slightly different to your left arm. That's fine, just allow that same relaxation to run down your right arm, all the way down to your hand and the tips of your fingers, so that both arms are completely relaxed, loose, limp and heavy. As you continue to relax, just focus now on your breath and, as you breathe deeply and slowly, as you feel your chest raise and lower and you listen to the sound of my voice and any other noises, like doors banging, traffic going past or phones ringing, it all helps you to relax even more as you go deeper and deeper into a lovely state of relaxation.

Now, as you continue going deeper and deeper, just focus on your tummy muscles; it's here we hold onto our gut feelings, tensions and our anxieties, so really relax those tummy muscles now ... that's right ... and now just shift your focus to the back of your head and the back of your neck and allow that relaxation to run down the back of your head, the back of your neck, all the way down your spine, all the way down to your hips and your thighs. As you feel yourself drifting deeper and deeper, allow that relaxation to run down your right leg, all the way down to your foot and the tips of your toes, so that your right leg feels totally relaxed, loose and limp and heavy. Now just allow that same relaxation to run down your left leg, all the way down to your foot and the tips of your toes, so that your left leg is completely relaxed, loose and limp and heavy. So now both legs, both arms and the whole of your body is totally relaxed and, in a moment or two, I'm just going to count down from ten to one and, as I do so, you'll find with every number you'll become ten times more relaxed than you are now ... ten ... going down ... nine ... deeper and deeper ... eight ... seven, so relaxed now ... six, five, and the more you can relax the deeper you can go and the deeper you go the more you can relax ... four ... that's right, deeper and deeper ... one, now totally relaxed and, as you're now totally relaxed and, as you listen to my voice, there is no need to strain to listen, just relax and let go of all your thoughts and worries and just let this be effortless ... ...

★(There now follows a passage of language ambiguity to completely confuse and bypass any resistance to access the subconscious mind by the conscious mind.)

... and by doing so you may find the inner power to reason all the many ways to establish the things that will carry you forward to access the parts of your mind that

hold the keys to open all the doors of opportunity and, when you open the doors, you will find these opportunities to access those abilities that will change your future that stems from a knowledge that will come later, so you really can find the wealth, the understanding and the depth of all the resources of your subconscious mind, giving you a sense of confidence and inner knowledge and the insights which leads you to know that … …

Change isn't hard or difficult, it's just SO EASY, yes it really IS EASY, in fact, it's just a choice, a decision, just a choice that you have already made to (… issue …), so isn't it wonderful you have decided to take back your control this way and that way and any other way you can find to make that change? It's now an opportunity for you to make that change and to make it permanent, because all change SIMPLY begins with you.

So now, YOUR UNCONSCIOUS already knows what it needs to know to make those changes, just give yourself permission to relax completely, so you can EASILY achieve all your goals NOW. You may wait for it to happen, or it may have already happened NOW. In a moment or two, I'm going to count from one to three and, when I get to three, I'm going to ask you to open your eyes. After a few moments, I'm going to ask you to close them again and, every time you close your eyes, you'll find that you just simply double your relaxation.

So, one, two, three … eyes open … eyes closed … doubling your relaxation now, going deeper and deeper, that's right … one … two … three … eyes open … eyes closed … sinking and sinking all the way down, one, two, three … eyes open … eyes closed … deeply, deeply relaxed now … and, as you go deeper and deeper down, my voice can just drift into the background, it's really not that important, what's more important is that you make the changes that are important to you and I'm going to make it really EASY for you. Now, in a moment, I'm going to count from five down to one and, when I get to one, you'll be in a very special part of your subconscious mind where all change takes place and anything I say to that special part of your subconscious mind for your benefit cannot be easily removed and it will stay with you, helping and guiding you to make any changes you desire EASILY and PERMANENTLY, so ready … … five … going down … four … deeper and deeper … three … so relaxed … two … down to that special place … one … where all change takes place … and now you're deep within this special part of your subconscious mind, just give yourself permission to succeed ... (pause) and now that you have given yourself permission to succeed, amazing, incredible changes will now take place ... (now tell the client's subconscious mind the changes the client wishes to make).

Diminishing anxiety

This script is designed to support people through
the pandemic or any type of worry or anxiety where
the client feels a loss of control.

Norah Mahony

Gently close your eyes and begin to relax into this moment, welcoming in peace, bit by bit. Right now, allow yourself a moment to acknowledge what you're feeling. You don't have to take an inventory of all your thoughts ... or call out all your fears ... Just sit with the sensation of your anxiety ...

Maybe it feels stuck in your throat or in your chest ... Is it in your head? Your stomach? Or right near your heart? Just stay with it ... And feel what it feels like.

Perhaps it feels sharp and burning ...

Or maybe dull and heavy ... Don't judge it. Simply allow it to be ...

It wants to help. And in its own misguided way, it's trying to ...

Know that there are millions if not billions of other people sitting with this same weight in their chest, this same sensation in their heads and body, right now ...

We're all trying to figure out life ... Trying to see our way through various crises.

And when this occurs, anxiety comes ... to help. But without meaning to, it can actually hurt.

It can slow us down ... Create a fog ... fear ...

However, you don't have to let it take over ... You have a say in what goes on in your mind and soul ...

It's okay to feel what you're feeling, but if you allow anxiety to take over, it can suppress you; and you can say no to this happening ...

You are your best way through this ...

Inhale deeply, then use the exhale to shrink that anxiety ...

Notice that every time you breathe out, it gets a little smaller ...

That's how you come through ...

Your higher self, your rational self, your resourceful, calm and optimistic self ...

The self who's faced the unknown many times before and come out the other side ...

The one who has succeeded in the past when they didn't know how they would ...

You've been through so much and have overcome so much because you were built for it. You've survived every challenge life has thrown you thus far, and you're doing an amazing job of being human ...

Breathe that anxiety smaller ...

And breathe it smaller still ...

Notice how, with every exhale, it just shrinks and shrinks. You were built to overcome adversity, and you will overcome this ... Of course you will ...

You *are* overcoming this ...

You know this fact deeply and you accept this is just a phase ...

Even when outside events are out of your control, your thoughts are always yours to choose.

Wouldn't you agree that you have zero responsibility for things that are outside of your control?

You aren't responsible for predicting the future, other people's actions, controlling world events or manipulating outcomes ...

You can only do your best, and you're doing a great job ...

Your only responsibility is to control your own space, the space that's inside of you. And you can cultivate anything you want there; beauty, peace, love. By choosing your thoughts, you get to make it a safe space or a hostile one ... It's totally up to you ...

You choose to shrink your anxiety now, and expand your awareness ... You choose to reject any more downward mental spirals ... You choose to pick a more optimistic thought instead ...

You can't control, but you can choose ...

And as long as you choose according to your highest vision for yourself and others, you can create a safe space within yourself, even when turmoil is swirling around you …

You recognise that positive outcomes are possible …

You know you have demonstrated the ability to overcome adversity in the past … and because you can do those things, then you can shrink your anxiety down to a size you can manage. There's no need to let it manage you …

Take this moment, this one moment in time, to allow yourself a moment's peace …

Nothing that's happening is your fault …

Future outcomes are not your responsibility. So, give yourself the peace of being relieved from those burdens …

Your power is limited to what you can control, and right now you choose to control your inner space. You're using it to choose peace in this moment …

Can you remember a time when you felt hopeful? Grateful? Do you recall the feeling of having something to look forward to? Everyone can think of at least one time in their lives when things felt right and good. That energy is yours. It's available to you at any time. All you have to do is choose it.

So, choose that now. I'd like you to remember a time when things felt right or good in your life. Bring that picture into your mind's eye now and hold onto it for a few moments …

It can be something big like a great day out or a holiday, or something small, like a feeling you got spending time with someone you love …

Hold onto that feeling now … the feelings you get when things are going well for you …

You realise now that joining circumstances in their chaos is unhelpful. It's unhelpful to get stirred up with negativity that wants to bring you down with it …

Raise your vibration higher. Not in an effort to control, but as a gift to yourself …

You do this by choosing different thoughts, moment to moment … and feeling good inside …

So, continue to imagine that time in your life when things felt good and hold onto the feeling of contentment and the happiness it brings …

Feel your body expanding with those emotions now as you feel better, and happier and your vibration continues to rise higher and higher, happier and happier, peaceful and calm.

You deserve love at all times … peace at all times … hope at all times.

And you alone possess the power to give those things to yourself and to those around you.

Just breathe deeply … Feel your muscles relax deeper and deeper, your shoulders, jaw and whole body totally relaxed now …

Be here now.

And rejoice in the fact that you're safe in the present moment.

What's passed is passed … whatever will be will be … And ultimately, all will be well …

Just stay here. Stay right here in the present moment and remain here.

You have allowed yourself an emotion that feels better than anxiety today … well done …

You've done something amazing today. Even if you can only hold onto it for a few seconds … it's worth it … it's beautiful … and you are creating a more peaceful life.

You are creating something beautiful in yourself and in the world … By raising your vibration … you change the world … did you know that? Your thoughts are powerful …

And you deserve the best of thoughts … give yourself the beauty of high vibrational thoughts.

If you like, you can briefly revisit that anxious feeling you had earlier, and see that it's now diminished …

It's shrunk …

It's lost its colour, and the hurt is much smaller than before …

It's something you can manage …

You know that now …

And the more you hear these words, and this reminder … the more you realise you have the control …

Anxiety has and must submit itself to you because you are its master … not the other way around.

You have the control, and you let go of every pessimistic thought you have.

Instead, you're willing and able to choose better, because you deserve better …

In a moment you'll hear a countdown from ten to one.

When you hear the number one, you'll awaken to new feelings of calm and strength.

You will also feel refreshed and alert.

You'll recognise your ability to overcome adversity and achieve your dreams regardless of any distractions … Are you ready? Let's do this …

Ten, nine, eight, seven, six, five, four, three, two, one.

Feeling strong, in control and powerful … you are the master of you … and you've got this.

Earth, wind and fire

Escape from the stresses of the day

Diane Jennings

(Use chime background music if you can)

The elements are what make the world; it's so easy to forget the compounds that form every living being. Now you're resting so comfortably, I want you to imagine the sound of chimes, notice the feelings of peace passing over you, feel yourself becoming more and more relaxed. The wind gently blows, catching the chimes with every gentle gust. As you breathe out, notice how the chimes move in the breeze. The chimes are a perfect way to focus on the here and now. If thoughts pop into your mind, acknowledge them, but if you can, just let them go …

Imagine you're walking amongst the long grasses; watch as the grasses sway in the wind, feel the breeze on your face. You look up and notice tall, elegant trees, notice the leaves, what colour are they? They could be cool, calm greens, rich, rusty oranges, or crisp, soft browns. This place is a magical place, a place where you can leave all your troubles behind and immerse yourself in the nature all around. You notice how calm you feel; while you are in this space, nothing troubles you at all.

You walk further along, through the tall grasses, and you hear the sound of water; a gentle, steady flow of one of the Earth's most precious elements. You follow the path of the river as it meanders through the earth, you track its path like a moth tracks a moving light.

During your journey, you feel the warm sun on your face; picture the sun now, filling you with life and energy. The sun glistens on the water, creating a beautiful kaleidoscope of colour, a rainbow. Imagine this rainbow now, with a beginning, a middle and an end. Just like life. It's important to note that just like this rainbow, life is forever changing, and with it are our life experiences, these experiences can help us to be the best version of ourselves we possibly can be. Taking a moment here just to reflect on the most important things in our lives, holding on to those memories that have value to us, and letting go of those that have no positive meaning.

As you walk on, the warmth draws you nearer, the flicker of yellows, oranges and reds glow in the distance. The element of fire becoming more and more important, more and more necessary. You find the source of the warmth and nestle yourself down in a warm, comfortable place. You stare at the fire as it burns through the wood, you feel safe and protected. And you allow all those negative thoughts and feelings to go up with the smoke. Watch them as they drift away with the winds of time. Leaving you only with feelings of calm, strength and knowledge. Knowledge that you can cope with life's challenges by feeling confident, trusting your own judgement and doing what is best for you. You have your best interests at heart, and you know you will make the right decisions for you. In this way, you will feel calmer with every day that passes. Anticipate that calmness and calmness is yours.

In the woods

A guided relaxation

Paula Greensted

Now you're so nicely relaxed … your breathing becoming slower and steadier … feeling totally at ease and enjoying these moments all to yourself … a wonderful sense of peace and calmness washes over you as you allow your mind to drift and dream … I would like you to imagine, as vividly as you can, that you are standing in the middle of a beautiful woodland … surrounded by trees of every shape and size. Their branches form a lush green canopy overhead and you look up as a soft breeze whispers through the leaves … hearing the rhythmic sigh of the branches, swaying gently. It feels safe here … with the sweet sound of birdsong carried on the air … and as you listen carefully, you can just make out the call of a cuckoo somewhere in the distance.

The woodland is so inviting that you want to venture deeper … exploring the beautiful landscape … and, as you go deeper and deeper … you breathe in the earthy scent of moss as you walk, the ground soft beneath your feet … dappled sunlight playing on the verdant grass ahead.

The grass borders a winding shingle path, and you follow it at a leisurely pace … enjoying the comfortable warmth of the day … knowing there is nowhere else you have to be and nothing you need to do except relax. The sweet, heady fragrance of honeysuckle fills your senses as you stroll and then you find yourself among a flourish of wildflowers … in a kaleidoscope of colour … golden yellow celandine, red campion and foxgloves too … their pink and purple heads like tiny trumpets. White butterflies alight upon the leaves, elegantly opening their wings … while busy bees hum their way purposefully from petal to petal … and you watch, fascinated … marvelling at how each little bloom is unique and special … adding their own individual beauty to this magical place. You realise that every living thing here, be it large or small, has its part to play … everything is valued … important.

This joyful thought lifts your spirits and, moving on, you find yourself relaxing more and more deeply with each step you take … letting go of all troubles and anxieties … feeling them all fade away as you roam … surrounded by the harmony and balance of nature.

Twigs snap underfoot as you approach a large shape up ahead, veiled by a column of hazy sunlight … and there before you stands a magnificent old oak tree … perhaps the biggest oak tree you have ever seen … strong and majestic. It seems to draw you in, and you reach out to touch its furrowed bark, rough and warm beneath your fingertips. You lean yourself against this grand old tree that has stood in this spot for so many years … decade after decade … its roots firm and solid … and a deep tranquility grows within you, expanding … a sublime sense of oneness with nature. It is almost as if you can hear the ancient tree's heartbeat along with your own … slow, steady and strong … filling you with wonder as you rest against its thick, rugged trunk … feeling so safe … so supported. You breathe deeply, absorbing the strength and resilience of this wise, sturdy oak … relishing the moment as you give yourself up to the peace and serenity of this glorious wood.

When you look around once more, a flash of red catches your eye and you notice a little robin, half-concealed among the leaves on a nearby shrub. It appears to watch you too … tilting its head … and you smile. It sings as you wander on … the sound echoing faintly behind you … like a blessing.

You become aware of the rush and babble of water in the distance, growing louder as you explore further. This entices you and you follow the sound until you come upon a clearing … where a gurgling stream glints like a silver ribbon, unfurling in the sunshine. It feeds down into a large pool, fringed by rich vegetation, and there a willow tree leans tenderly down to drape its slender leaves beneath the surface. The splash and murmur of the water is soothing … so you sit yourself down on the bank, resting back against a large rock worn smooth by time, and gaze into the blue-green depths of the pool, all tension simply ebbing away as the sun warms the top of your head … and you begin to feel drowsy … your eyelids becoming heavier and heavier … until you just drift off into a lovely daydream.

You dream you are floating on a fluffy white cloud above the woodland, suspended in a sky of brilliant blue ... watching other clouds gliding gently past ... unhurried ... serene. You take pleasure in a delicious sense of lightness and ease ... floating and drifting with no fears or worries ... only a sense of wonder and delight at how effortlessly you are moving. You look upon the wood and the glittering pool that lie just below you ... you could almost brush the treetops with your fingertips ... and it feels good to know that you can see things from another perspective ... a different view. You ponder on the abundance of the wood, that stately oak tree, the beautiful flowers, the sparkling stream, the tranquil pool ... and recognise a dawning sense of appreciation for everything around you. You realise that, in this very moment, you have all that you need ... you are safe ... supported ... strengthened ... part of everything around you. You are enough.

Soon, the cloud on which you are resting begins to float softly downward and, as it touches the ground, you are back beside the pool ... droplets of cool water spraying lightly on your skin as the stream courses through. You feel refreshed ... calm ... relaxed ... perfectly at ease ... perhaps more so than ever before. You sit up and look around once more ... noticing how the sun has travelled further across the sky ... shadows moving across the ground. You inch closer to the edge of the pool and peer down into its rippled surface ... seeing your own reflection looking back up. You appear different somehow ... your expression softer ... composed ... more confident ... your true self. There is a smile playing on your lips ... and you feel lighter ... freer ... in control ... seeing everything more clearly ... secure in the knowledge that you have all the capability and resources you need to accomplish the things you want to achieve. You have inner strength ... and resilience ... like the oak tree. And you know that, whenever you need to, whenever you want to recharge or relax, you can return to this wonderful place of peace, calm and tranquility, simply by calling to mind this magical woodland and the strength of that wise, majestic oak tree. Better still, you will be delighted at just how good you feel when you return to normal conscious awareness ... rested ... soothed ... and strengthened.

Mountain meditation

Changing perspective

Diane Jennings

Observe your breathing; no need to change it, just notice it. Allow your body to be still, sitting with a sense of dignity and resolve, a sense of being complete, whole. In this very moment, with your posture reflecting your sense of calmness, you feel the anticipation rising.

As you sit there, picture in your mind's eye, as best you can, the most beautiful mountain that you know or that you have ever seen. Allowing it to become clear in your mind's eye, its lofty peak high in the sky, the large base of rock rooted into the earth's crust, its steep or gently sloping sides. Notice how massive it is and solid. And how beautiful it appears. Perhaps your mountain has snow at the top and trees on the lower slopes; perhaps it has one prominent peak or a series of peaks or a high plateau.

While you sit there with this image of your mountain in your mind's eye, take a small step forward, feeling the ground beneath your feet. Feel how it supports you, firm and solid. You start navigating the majestic mountain, knowing that you will reach the top. You are all prepared and ready, you have your boots on, your bag on your back and you are looking forward to the journey. This climb to the mountaintop is like your journey in life. It may seem daunting if you look too far ahead; looking how far you've come will not help you make progress. But if you focus on each step you take, just like life itself, you will get there. If you worry about the future or the past then you can be caught in a trap of negative thinking, but if you focus on the here and now, this very moment, you can enjoy the journey.

You place one foot in front of another. You breathe in the calm, cool air, feel it on your face. You hear the sound of an eagle soaring in the sky. You hear the rustle of the grass beneath your feet. You look up and notice the movement of the clouds. And, without realising it, you've reached the top of the misty mountain. And it's while you're here, you realise you have the key to success in life, you know what is the right way for you. Your journey up this magnificent mountain is filled with challenges and obstacles; the ever-changing weather, the ever-changing terrain. But you know you have all the equipment you need to overcome these difficulties, just like in life. You know the key to success is to remain calm, to navigate the small stones and boulders without frustration, without anger as you realise these are not helpful. You allow all your worries and cares to fade away, float away with the winds of time, as you realise you have complete control in the way to go. You can choose which is the right path for you. You glance down while at the summit of this beautiful, peaceful mountain, sit down on a small, smooth boulder, you look up and notice the ever-changing clouds, have you ever noticed this?

The maze

A metaphor to free the mind, remove mental blockages
and encourage perspective change

Elaine Neale

One day the breeze was playing as it roamed the countryside. As it swooped through a canyon it came across a maze of rock, the huge boulders forming towering alleyways. In the centre of the maze sat a young woman, her shoulders hunched, her head in her hands. Seeing the young woman looking so sad and distressed, the breeze swept down to see what was the matter, circling her and gently lifting her hair as it did so. The young woman lifted her face and, with a small, sad smile, allowed the breeze to caress it.

The young woman sighed. "Ah, I wish I was free to sweep through the canyon like you, Breeze! Then I could leave this maze and travel beyond the canyon to where the land is green."

"This maze has many exits, I could see them from above. Why don't you explore and find one?" replied the breeze.

"The routes through and out of the maze are all blocked," said the woman, "I cannot find a way through, so I must stay here in this uncomfortable place."

The breeze considered this and was puzzled. It had seen no blockages or barriers to trap the woman as it swooped over and around the maze.

"Show me," the breeze requested.

The young woman rose from the slab of rock she had been seated upon and walked over to the nearest path from the centre of the maze, stopping before she reached it.

"There, you see?" she asked the breeze.

The breeze brushed against the woman's shoulder and it did indeed appear that the way was blocked. The breeze moved forward and felt only the cold, rough surface of rock.

As the breeze again considered this puzzle, it eddied from side to side. As it moved further to the left, it cried out, "Look! Come over here and see!"

As the woman walked over to the left it became clear that what had appeared to be solid rock, blocking the way, was in fact overlapping boulders that, while appearing solid from the front, had a pathway between them. Standing a little taller, the woman took her first tentative steps onto the revealed pathway and smiled.

"Oh, thank you!" she said to the breeze, "I couldn't see that before!"

The young woman trailed her fingers along the surface of the rock walls as she moved forward to find the next opening. On and on she went, finding openings that she could not see at first, going over, under, around ... moving further from the centre of the maze where she had been trapped for so long. Sometimes curtains – heavy or gossamer thin – gave the illusion of a dead end, but as she touched them, they drew apart, revealing the onward path. The path grew ever wider and brighter, offering more options and choices for the woman. And, as she walked with the breeze, further and further out of the maze, the young woman found that, with each step, each barrier conquered and decision made, she held herself more erect, lifting her eyes to the world around her and moved with greater confidence.

When they reached the last circle of the maze, the rock walls were no longer tall or imposing and had instead become a low wall, small enough to simply step over. As she did so, the young woman laughed and raised her arms to the breeze in joy.

"Thank you for showing me the way out!"

The breeze swirled around her, sharing her joy and excitement and replied, "I only showed you a different perspective. You found the way out yourself!"

The young woman's eyes sparkled, she smiled her response and set off, with the breeze at her back, out of the stone canyon and into the lush green of the world beyond.

Three good things

A guided relaxation to boost positivity by promoting
three simple positives each day

Anne Gregory

You can be aware of all parts of your body ... mentally scan slowly down ... from the top of your head to the tips of your toes ... and acknowledge how every part of your body feels ... ...

Notice the parts which are beginning to relax first ... and encourage them to relax further ... ...

Notice if there are any parts of your body that are still holding tension ... if so ... allow those muscles to relax too ... ...

Some parts may take a little longer or may need a little more encouragement ... but that is okay ... there is no rush ... you have all the time in the world, and you can take as long as you need ... ...

As you relax more ... feel your body softening and sinking down even more ... ...

It is such a lovely feeling to have ... total relaxation ... whenever you want it ... ...

So ... as you begin to relax ... I would like you to think of a favourite place ... ...

It can be anywhere at all ... ...

Somewhere you go to on a regular basis ... ...

Somewhere you went to once before ... ...

Somewhere you would love to go to ... ...

Or somewhere you have created in your imagination ... ...

And just bring that place to mind now ... ...

See the place in the eye of your mind ... very clearly ... ...

Picture your surroundings ... in great detail ... ...

Be aware of the sounds you might hear ... here ... ...

Imagine yourself there ... now ... ...

Visualise the colours that are all around you ... ...

See yourself ... ...

See what you are doing ... ...

Feel the sensations you associate with this favourite place ... ...

Keep thinking of this place as I begin to count down ... from 3 ... ...

You are feeling even more relaxed ... as you start to sink deeper ... 2 ... ...

That picture ... very vivid in your mind ... going deeper ... and deeper ... and deeper ... 1 ... ...

So relaxed now ...

Both your mind and your body in the perfect place ... at the perfect time ... ...

The perfect result of your commitment to relax ... and unwind ... and open your mind ... ...

As you open your mind to the endless opportunities ... and the infinite possibilities ... awaiting you ... ...

Because you can develop beneficial habits ... that can bring all of those opportunities and all of those possibilities into your awareness ... enabling you to select the ones you want ... and turn them into your reality ... ...

Allowing you to get the results you desire ... in the area of your life that you want to focus on ... ...

Setting up the perfect conditions ... to make achieving whatever you want as simple as can be ... ...

Just like ... if you had a physical goal that you wanted to attain ... maybe losing weight ... or toning up ... or building stamina ... ...

You may choose to create an exercise plan for yourself ... or you may join a gym ... ...

And you know that ... simply by creating the plan ... or by joining a gym ... you will not achieve your goal ... ...

You will achieve success by putting in the routines ... and the habits ... that make the changes possible ... ...

To create the positive changes you require ... ...

You need to be consistent ... with your commitment ... ...

You need to be repetitive in your activities ... ...

You need to be true to your target ... ... goal ... ... results ... ...

And ... just as with any physical goal ... your mind is its very own muscle ... ...

That needs to be exercised ... and flexed ... and worked out ... ...

As you work out ... the muscle which can help you to create and embed positive habits into your life ... ...

To improve your well-being ... ...

Very simply by committing to some easy tasks each day ... ...

Three good things every day ... ...

By choosing to think positive thoughts every day ... ...

Whereby changing your perspective ... to allow you to see things from a different angle ... ...

And ... if any negative thoughts try to creep in ... you can change them to something more beneficial ... or distract yourself with something better ... ...

You really do have the ability to make that change ... and reap that reward ... ...

By choosing to think positive thoughts every day ... ...

You can choose to prioritise yourself every day ... and do something you want to do ... just for you ... ...

Perhaps an activity you enjoy ... or a hobby you love ... ...

Bringing joy on every level ... ...

Physically helping you to relax ... and generating some feel-good chemicals in your body ... and you deserve it ... ...

And when you make time for yourself ... and feel good ... everyone around you benefits too ... ...

Simply by choosing to prioritise you every day ... ...

And you can decide to spend time with the positive people in your life ... ...

Who make you feel supported ... and appreciated ... and boosted every single day ... ...

Enjoying the company of those people who uplift you ... who love you ... and who you love too ... ...

You deserve that ... ...

You deserve to spend time with the positive people in your life ... ...

You are worthy of all the good things in life ... ...

Just decide to prioritise yourself ... every ... single ... day ... ...

And discover how much better you feel ... today ... tomorrow ... and forever ... ...

CHAPTER THREE

Finding balance in nature

Autumn senses

This visualisation will take you on a beautiful tranquil autumn country walk, allowing you to relieve stress and shift your mood to one of relaxation

Emma Last

When you are ready, close your eyes. Let the weight of your body ground with the space that you are sitting or lying on and start to let any tension float out of your body. Start by breathing deeply into your heart and deeper into your abdomen, hold for a couple of seconds and breathe out. Slowly push the breath out of your body. Repeat until you start to feel yourself relax.

You are about to start your walk. Imagine you are walking along a path in a country park on a bright sunny autumn day. There are trees lining the path and, as you walk, you feel more and more relaxed, and any worries float away. You are enjoying feeling more clarity and more relaxed with every step you take. You feel the freshness of the day as you breathe in each breath.

You notice a small path to the left, which you decide to take, and you find yourself in a densely wooded area. This place is where you are able to connect further with your inner calm and, as you walk further into the woodland, the deeper and deeper you fall into your relaxation. You are taking your time.

You breathe deeply and feel the relaxation flow through your body.

You want to savour all of the details. You are using all of your senses to appreciate the beauty of the woodland. Your eyes take in the tall trees all around you. You take in the beautiful silver tones of the birch. You look up and see the sun shining through the gaps in the trees.

You see that the red, brown and yellow tones of the leaves create a canopy above your head. You notice leaves falling from the trees, spinning and twirling as they slowly fall to the ground. As they touch the ground, you notice a blanket of leaves under your feet.

You take in your surroundings, breathe in every detail …

You hear the snap of twigs that have also fallen from the trees. The birds are calling a variety of different sounds. The trees are dancing and swaying in the light breeze, and you can hear the flow of a stream not too far away.

Take in your surroundings, breathe in the sounds …

You take a few steps and notice that you are treading carefully; you can feel and hear the leaves crunching between your feet. As you walk, the feel of the crunch under feet lessens and you realise that you must be close to the stream as the leaves have a wetness. You reach out to touch a huge tree. You can feel the softness and smoothness and the areas where the bark feels rough against your fingers.

There is a gentle breeze, and you can feel the coldness on your face, yet the sun is strong enough for you to feel the nourishment and soothing of the warmth on your head, shoulders and back.

It is so peaceful. You love the calm and the relaxing feelings that this space brings.

Take your time … Breathe in every little detail …

You taste a freshness in your mouth from the mint you ate a few minutes ago. As you breathe in, you smell the scent of what you can only describe as autumn.

You are at peace. You are relaxed. Your whole body is relaxed. You are grateful for autumn days like these.

You take a few moments to appreciate and enjoy your deep sense of relaxation.

Take your time … Breathe in all the detail around you and, when you are ready, start to retrace your steps, walking back to the main path.

Feel how relaxed, calm and re-energised you feel right now. Savour these feelings of relaxation.

Start to become aware of the surface beneath you. When you are ready, open your eyes and start to take in your surroundings. Bring your awareness back to the present and the room you are in. Hold onto those feelings of relaxation as you carry on with your day.

Buzzy busy bees

Guided relaxation to focus on breathing

Diane Jennings

Have you ever noticed how busy you can be, moving from job to job, thinking all the time, always planning what you're doing next? Sometimes it can become overwhelming, stressful and exhausting.

Take a moment now … this is your time to stop … take a deep breath in, breathe in, breathe out, breathe in, breathe out … Slow down for a while … Allow your body to rest … As your body rests, your mind rests with it.

Just imagine now you have all the time in the world … nothing to do but rest here for a while … Picture now a cool, calm forest, just settling down for the evening … the activity of the day is done … the animals are settling down … the warm sun is setting and there's a calm stillness on the forest floor.

You wander over to a fallen tree … you notice the moss on its bark; soft and moist. A small, intrigued insect takes a glance at you … You decide to sit down … take the weight off your feet for a while.

It's here … while you're resting … you realise the importance of time for yourself. Those precious moments in the day where you can stop … Rest … download the stresses of the day … think of nothing but the breath you breathe in, and the breath you breathe out. You realise here how important your breath is to you … how life sustaining it can be. When you're busy, stressed, or anxious – just like those busy bees flying from beautiful flower to beautiful flower – we forget to breathe in the most effective way. We breathe shallow and fast, causing stress in our bodies.

It's while you're resting here … you can really focus on the positive benefits of effective breathing … really notice how good it feels to inhale that crisp, forest air … Allowing it to fill you completely, you can smell the sweet scents of the fruits of the forest. You exhale now, long and slow, longer than you breathe in. With this exhalation, let go of all those negative feelings, all those worries and cares of the day. Notice how much lighter you feel now as you stand up from the fallen tree, able to notice the natural beauty all around you. You now feel more positive, more able to cope and alive.

Cosmic connection

A guided visualisation to connect with the Universe
and promote joyous well-being

Caroline Measures

Let's take a moment to tune into ourselves and just notice how you're feeling right now.

I'd like you to imagine a glowing golden-white light at the crown of your head, like your own miniature sun. Maybe it's the light from a diamond or a crystal, sparkling and radiating tiny rainbows all around. Or a fiery ball of energy that responds to you alone. Turn up the brightness. Make it bigger, brighter, bolder and even more beautiful than before. With every breath you take, the light is getting stronger and stronger, dazzling, beautiful. Allow yourself to rest here for a moment, bathing in the warm golden-white light that shines down on you with warmth and peace …

The golden-white light can spread down from your crown, down over your forehead, your face and the back of your head. You might feel warmth, coolness, tingling or just relaxing as it flows over your skin. Maybe you can become aware of your facial expression and release any tension that you find there. Try to relax your forehead, the tiny muscles around the eyes, your cheeks … allow your jaw to go slack and your tongue to come away from the roof of your mouth. Just relax …

That's right …

The golden-white light continues its journey of relaxation, flowing past your neck and throat, releasing anything that no longer serves you, anything you've held back. Just letting it all go now. The light spreads out across both shoulders and flows down both arms, past the elbows, easing past the delicate wrist-bones and into the hands and fingertips. If there are any areas of tension, flood them with the bright light on the in-breath and say to yourself "release" on the out-breath …

Allow the nourishing light to fill your chest and upper back, running down the length of the spine and radiating out on all sides to soothe the lower back, the belly, the pelvic area and all the organs inside. Picture the light filling you up from the inside out. And relaaax …

Spreading over the hips and down both legs, through the thick, strong thigh muscles, over the knees, down the calves, through the ankles and into the feet and toes. Let the golden-white light flow …

So now you are in a cocoon of golden-white light. You can rest here a while, enjoying the nurturing energy that fills and surrounds you …

(Pause for a few minutes.)

Focus in on the radiant heart-centre and the light that shines there. The beautiful shimmering light. On the next out-breath, you're going to breathe that golden-white light out from your heart-centre and send it on a journey down into the Earth. Breathe in and breathe out, sending the golden-white light deep down into Mother Earth. Down through the earth, down through the rocks and all the way down to the molten core at the centre. Visualise this connection with Mother Earth. Sending love, energy, peace and harmony from your heart to hers. Also send her anything that you want to release, anything that needs to be transmuted back into loving energy. Let go of any stress, any hurt, any pain. Let go of the worries, the overwhelm, the tension. Let it all go now …

Bring your attention back to the radiant heart-centre again. The beautiful shimmering light. On the next out-breath, you're going to breathe that golden-white light out from your heart-centre and send it on a journey up to the stars. Breathe in and breathe out, sending the golden-white light high up into the universe above. Up through the clouds, up through space and all the way up to the twinkling stars. Maybe one star attracts your attention more than the others? Visualise a connection with it or with them all. Sending love, energy, peace and harmony from your heart to theirs. Bathe the stars in your golden light. Watch it swirling around them in a magical haze. Enjoy the playful energy of the stars and rest here a moment …

We're going to take that starlight energy and pull it down through space, down through the ethers and in through the crown of your head. What does it feel like coming in through your crown? Is it warm like the sun? Or tingling? Or like a cool breeze? Or maybe there are no sensations at all. Does it come in waves, or spirals? Is it a beam of light? Whatever it is, it's perfect for you right now.

Bring the starlight into your body and allow it to mix with your own golden-white light. See the shades of gold, silver, white, platinum and everything in between mingle and blend. Let it bathe every cell of your being and the air around you too. With every breath you take, more and more starlight comes down from above and enters through your crown. Your whole body can hold this light mix now, feeling so relaxed, so deeply at peace …

Let's take this beautiful blend of light from above and send it down into Mother Earth, uniting the stars with the earth below. Let it flow out of your feet and spread out across the land, flooding the world around you with golden light. Send it down, down, down deep into the ground. Down through the layers of soil and rock. Down and out through the rivers, lakes, seas and oceans. See the light mixing once again, this time merging with the green light of the natural world, creating a golden, silvery, green. The light of the forests. The light of the animal kingdom. The light of the land, the water. It's all here now.

Creating harmony and balance around us, creating harmony and balance within. Let's take this cosmic mix that you've helped to create and draw it back up through your feet and legs, up through your torso, up your neck, into your head and up out of the crown of your head. Let the light shine bright as it reaches higher and higher up into the sky. The golden-green energy shoots upwards towards the stars until it reaches the sparkling canopy above and spreads out to form a blanket in the night sky. As above, so below.

Use your breath to create an infinite cycle of natural harmony. Breathing in, draw up the green light from below. Breathing out, send it up to the universe above where it mixes with the starlight. On the next in-breath, bring the light blend back down in through your crown and, on the out-breath, radiate it down through your feet into the earth. A beautiful cycle of co-creation that energises and rejuvenates your cells, filling you with loving energy and the essence of who you are. Total relaxation. This is how it should be. You are in perfect balance right now. Feeling safe and grounded. Feeling secure and peaceful. In an expanded state of awareness. Continue breathing the light up and down … in and out … up and down … in and out … No need to try to control your breathing in any way. Just let it happen naturally and in your own time …

The flow of light will continue all by itself. For now, it's time for you to come back ever so slowly to the present moment. Start to become aware of the weight of your body sitting or lying just where you are. Notice the points of contact between your body and the surface. In your mind's eye, feel your way over your body and feel the weight of your clothes or blanket, the temperature of your skin – is it cool or warm? Notice any sounds around you now, any movement, any sensations. You can bring some gentle movement into your feet and hands, perhaps wiggling your toes and fingers, and circling your wrists and ankles. You might want to take a nice stretch as you take a deep breath in and slowly open your eyes as you breathe out again. Welcome back to the present moment feeling fully relaxed and refreshed!

Look up

A progressive muscle relaxation script encouraging us to lift our gaze and appreciate the relaxing and grounding connection to the natural world

Elaine Neale

Imagine yourself standing in a glade surrounded by trees, the sky visible in the opening above. It's a beautiful day ... not too hot ... and the trees shade you. The grass and earth are cool beneath your feet. You're relaxed and comfortable.

Now, take your gaze from the grass around you and lift your chin ... look up. The trees shade your eyes from the sun while allowing its rays to greet you ... see the world beyond. Not looking at the ground or even straight ahead ... look up. Take a deep, cleansing breath ... allow it to calm and relax you ... look up ... feel the breeze on your face ... the sun gently warming you ... the solid earth beneath your feet grounding and centring you.

See the bark on the trunks of the trees as you slide your gaze upward. The roughness easing as it spreads out into branches and twigs. Feel the energy as water surges from roots ... through trunk and branch ... out to the leaves ... leaves, dancing in the wind ... shimmering in different hues as they're ruffled in the sunshine ... creating pockets of darkness and quickly shifting patches of colour and glittering light ... an ever-changing canopy above you, reaching out over the glade as if stretching to meet friends around the other side.

Moving your gaze out to the farthest tips of the leaves, your gaze is caught by clouds, lazily drifting across the sky ... you track their progress for a moment, watching them appear from behind the branches above you and make their way across the wide-open sky before, once again, disappearing beyond the trees at the far side of the glade. You feel their calm … their freedom. Almost as if that freedom of movement is being shared with you … brought down to you by the sunlight that passes over them before meeting your upturned face.

You absorb the sunlight and feel it flow down within you like a waterfall of light, bringing immense calm and relaxation.

It starts with a tingle at the top of your head as you breathe deeply … drinking in the fresh scents of the day. The tingle becomes a warm glow, spreading its fingers across your scalp and easing the tension from it. It's such a beautiful feeling … you can't help but relax as the tension releases.

Another deep, slow breath and you can feel yourself relaxing more and more. Any time you want to go deeper or relax more … just take that deep … slow … breath … allow your muscles to go limp … and exhale the tension … as you just … relax.

That warm glow spreads down from your scalp to your forehead … easing away any worry lines … there's no need to frown when you're this relaxed. Feel your eyebrows slide back to a neutral position … moving on … to release the tension around your eyes … all those little muscles releasing and relaxing … and your cheeks … and around your mouth … and chin … tension falling away. It's okay if your mouth drops open a little … your face in repose.

Moving round to the back of your head … down through your hair and down your neck … an area that can carry so much tension … relax the muscles in your neck. Give your neck a gentle stretch … allow your breath to extend that delicious warmth into your neck muscles … relaxing more and more as it spreads all the way down your neck and across the top of your shoulders … and your upper back … allowing your shoulders to drop down and back into an entirely natural … and comfortable … position.

Warmth and relaxation spills over your shoulders and down through your arms … down your upper arms … eddying around your elbows … before enveloping your lower arms … easing wrists and fingers too. Your arms feel wonderfully heavy … not having to hold anything … it's as though you can feel unwanted tension dripping from the ends of your fingers and thumbs. You might want to wiggle your fingers and send those drops of tension sprinkling to the ground … you're done with them … so shake them off … let the ground take them and make them into something new and useful.

While you were focused on your arms, that relaxing warmth has also been spreading down your back ... feel it moving slowly down ... relaxing the muscles either side of your spine and around your ribs and chest ... it's like putting on a favourite jumper on a cold day ... so warm and soft ... comforting. Relaxation spreads down to your waist and lower back ... gently stretch and arch your back until you feel the relaxation. It feels so good ... just to relax.

Use your breath to release your chest. Let the muscles relax and your chest inflate as fully as you can ... before exhaling, slowly and completely. Relax the muscles in your stomach ... down around your hips and bottom. Feel the sunlight easing the muscles in your legs ... flowing down your thighs ... your knees ... ankles ... feet ... and toes ... letting those last drops of tension seep into the ground ... leaving you ... completely ... relaxed ... calm ... and infused with the refreshing, peaceful energy of the sunlight ... face upturned to the sky ... mind and body calm, relaxed and in tune.

Take a few moments ... ...

Floating with your thoughts ... ...

Enjoying this feeling of complete relaxation and balance ... ...

Until ... you gradually become aware of the glade and the cool feeling of the earth beneath your feet once again.

The sun is dipping and day is turning to night. The day is cooling, but wrapped in this magical blanket of sunshine and relaxation, you're not at all cold. You're content ... as you look up ... and see the first stars starting to twinkle in the evening sky ...

Look up to the stars and take a few moments just to ... relax and rest.

The waterfall

A guided relaxation taking you through the discovery
of a mystical hidden waterfall

Elaine Neale

Let me take you to a wonderfully relaxing place ... a place of sights, sounds and smells where you can safely let your imagination soar ...

I'd like you to imagine that you're out for a walk in the countryside. You're heading uphill, nearly at the crest ... it's an easy climb and you're enjoying the sounds of the birds and the swish of the long grass either side of the path. Wildflowers are dotted along the verge, their bright colours peeping out between the tall stems ... yellow ... purple ... white ... pink and blue tones in jewel-like glimpses. The hill rises higher to your left, obscuring the view to that side, and sweeps downhill on your right, in an expanse of wild grasses ... before dropping into a valley, heavy with foliage.

As the hill rises, you can see the tower of an ancient castle emerge over the top of the grass, up the hill to the left. Although slowly decaying, it's still beautiful, holding its once commanding position atop the hill with quiet strength. A rough gravel path leads up to the arched entrance to the castle courtyard, moss now growing on the mottled stones. You can see steps, steep and narrow, pulling up from the courtyard, running up to defensive towers, battlements or the castle keep itself. Certainly a centre of activity and power in the past, but now gentling into a romantic vista, welcoming visitors rather than repelling invaders ... You smile to yourself, imagining the lives and encounters of those who have lived here in centuries past ... the day-to-day clamour of a busy castle in the midst of the peaceful countryside.

Exploring the castle is tempting but it's not where you want to go just yet ... maybe you'll come back later, or another day. Today your route takes you along this path, below the castle sitting so proudly at the top of the hill. The path starts to wend its way downhill, narrowing as it does so. It's more a track of compacted earth now, packed hard by years of feet. The hill becomes much steeper as you go on. The bank to your left rises up sharply like a grassy cliff as the path plunges down into the valley, and you start to see the tops of trees, growing far below you to the right. The path requires care but you know that it's safe. There's even a sturdy fence and handrail to help you.

The air is changing now ... cool and moist. Gone is the wide-open sky from the top of the hill as the bank and trees begin to envelop you ... it's like entering a magical world. The sun is dappled through the trees, twinkling through and casting shafts of light onto the lush green foliage around you. It's darker in here, shady ... making it a special and secret place as though filled with myth and magic. So many shades of green and brown surround you. Trees and ferns taking over from the grass.

You can hear the sound of water; first a powerful rushing sound but backed by the gurgling and babbling of slower-moving water. You can hear it ... smell it ... almost taste it in the air but you can't see it yet. It's still shrouded by the deep green leaves of the trees around you ... a promise of beauty yet to come.

Every now and again there is a short flight of wooden steps built into the path, easing your way down the steep slope, carrying you over sections that you might find too difficult. Perfectly safe and secure ... nothing will harm you here.

You descend through the trees lining the path, beneath the level of their boughs, and catch your first glimpse of the waterfall through the array of tree trunks. It cascades from the top of the ravine in a gushing torrent ... freefalling from a staggering height before plunging into the dark waters of the basin below. A myriad of tiny droplets hang in the air, creating a fine mist that refracts the light ... forming multitudes of rainbow flashes.

In the basin, the collected water appears dark, almost black, with white, frothy bubbles created by the water's furious descent. It swirls and tumbles before continuing downstream. Beneath the basin, the river widens ... the water slows and babbles over stones and rocks in the riverbed. Your path has brought you safely to the bottom of the ravine and looking up you can see just how far you've come from that sunny, grassy hilltop ... down into this world of wonder and movement. The path circles around and brings you over a wooden bridge across the river, revealing the full splendour of the towering waterfall, easily as tall as the castle tower. You rest your hands on the mossy handrail of the bridge as you pause to admire the waterfall. Cool and damp but reassuringly solid; the handrail reinforces the feeling of safety, grounding you and bringing you peace.

Following the water down, your eyes alight on a small, pebbled area, a bit like a beach, at the edge of the wide river where the water quietens, the water not reaching it at this time of year. It's undoubtedly fully submerged when the river is in full spate but, at this time of year, it's exposed ... and the perfect place to reach the water's edge. The path leads right to it, encouraging you to visit. You give in to the impulse. You have plenty of time to indulge your curiosity ... all the time in the world, it seems. It's almost as if time has stopped since you climbed down the ravine, leaving time, cares and concerns at the top ... out of reach ... no need to worry about anything ... time down here is just for you and moves only at the pace you want it to. You can spend as long as you like here, in this magical place ... all the while knowing that you'll be right on time when you choose to ascend to the top again.

Reaching the pebbles, you pick one up. It's smooth to the touch, shaped by years in the riverbed and striated with ribbons of colour ... silver ... grey ... black and brown. Its weight, comforting in your hand as you trace your thumb over its rounded edges. This pebble seems to embody the feeling of this place ... the water, energised by its frenetic fall but now calm ... the deep, earthy, grounding scent ... the lush, relaxing greenery ... even the little rainbows sparkling joyously in the mist created by the waterfall. Perhaps you'll slip it in your pocket and take it home with you ... a little reminder of the wonder and calm of this place ... there to centre and ground you any time ... wrap it in your hand or take it out to look at ... something to anchor you to this place ... this feeling of complete peace and relaxation.

Drawing your attention away from the pebble, you look downstream. You can see the river under and past the bridge. It continues on its way, heading further down the ravine, surging over several rocky weirs as it makes its way lower. The trees in the distance form an arch over the river ... a natural vaulted roof ... hushed, cathedral-like and serene ... the water getting calmer and quieter the further it goes. Perhaps another day you'll follow the path downstream to where it disappears from view … maybe further … following the path of the river and revealing its story. Right now, you're perfectly content where you are … drinking in the power of the waterfall behind you … the sights and smells. Trailing your fingers in the cool water as it passes you on its journey, allowing it to take the last remnants of tension from your body and mind … and leaving only a feeling of energised tranquillity and complete peace of mind.

CHAPTER FOUR

Healing

Eyes -
rest from seeing & looking

- listen to yoga nidra spoken

Practice session w/
      instruments

Rhythm
chimes
shakers @ end

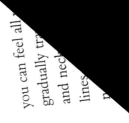

Coastal wal

A guided relaxation to uplift and revitalise, encouraging a broader perspective by reconnecting us to nature's rhythms

Paula Greensted

When you're ready, you can begin by focusing on your breathing for a moment or two. Notice the gentle rise and fall of your chest as you breathe in deeply through your nose … and then out in a long, slow exhalation … letting that happen easily … naturally … maybe noting how the air feels cooler as you inhale … and then warmer as you breathe out. Now think about your eyelids … how perhaps they are starting to feel heavy … and you might want to close them … when you're ready … resting your eyes … relaxing and enjoying these moments all for yourself. Nobody is wanting anything … nothing is expected of you … in fact, there is nothing at all for you to do except to relax back … knowing your body is fully supported … and you are safe. You can hear the sounds around you, inside the room and beyond … but these won't disturb you. In fact, they can actually help you to relax more deeply … reminding you that the world is still happily going about its business … so you can allow yourself to take a little time out to relax and recharge.

I would like you to bring your attention now to the very top of your head … and picture a beautiful warm light shining down on you there … perhaps in your favourite colour … and as that light shines down on the top of your head, notice how it begins to soothe all those little muscles in your scalp … allowing them to soften and relax … a good feeling. And as the light continues to flow, bathing you in that beautiful warmth and colour …

your muscles softening, loosening and relaxing as the light ...vels down through every part of your body … over your face ..., smoothing out the skin and releasing any little frown or worry ... … easing all the muscles around your eyes … your cheeks … your ...ose and your mouth … so that you can unclench your teeth and allow your jaw to slacken too … then continuing on down … easing any strain across your shoulders … flowing down along the long muscles either side of your spine … down through your arms, your wrists, your hands and every finger … just letting go … releasing any tension in your stomach too … moving on down through your hips and pelvis … and down into your legs … along your thighs, knees, calves, ankles and all the way into your feet … that soft warm light travelling down from the top of your head to the very tips of your toes … leaving every part of you beautifully relaxed and perfectly at ease. You're aware of how much slower and steadier your breathing is becoming now too … as you relax more and more deeply … perhaps more deeply than you ever thought possible … drifting … dreaming … just allowing your mind to wander.

And now you are so delightfully relaxed … feeling calm and comfortable … I wonder if you can imagine yourself seated on an old wooden bench, its surface silvered by the seasons … positioned at the crest of a hill … looking out to sea. It is early morning … so quiet and peaceful … and the sky is streaked with vivid pinks and oranges as the sun gilds the horizon … as if rising from the sea. You can hear the sound of waves, rhythmic and soothing as they roll towards the bay that lies below … and you watch the foaming white surf as it fizzes over the sand. Gazing at the beauty that surrounds you, you feel uplifted … enjoying the solitude of your vantage point … feeling the weathered surface of the bench solidly beneath you. A soft breeze lifts your hair … stroking your skin … and you breathe in purposefully … catching the faint smell of salt … tasting it on your lips.

Seabirds call above and you look up to where a pair of kittiwakes are circling … rising and dipping as they ride a current of air … spreading their wings wide in effortless flight. You contemplate how it might feel to soar above the vast ocean so freely … looking down on the rugged cliffs and winding coastal path … swooping across the patchwork of green and gold fields that blanket the surrounding countryside … now scarfed in a soft morning mist. The thought is exhilarating and inspires you to move on … so you leave the bench and wander further along the track that meanders around the clifftops ... where an old signpost points the way. It feels good to be moving ... stretching your limbs and feeling the gravel path beneath your feet. You become aware of your chest expanding as you inhale the crisp, clean morning air ... filling your lungs with freshness ... breathing out anything unwanted. You feel lighter with each step you take ... more positive ... energised ... free.

Gorse and purple heather line the route, brushing against your legs as you walk, and there are wildflowers too ... dewdrops glistening on their leaves. The sun has begun its daily climb ... reflected in the sea like a mirror ... and you suddenly notice a flash of colour far out on the water ... a little red and white fishing boat bobbing in the distance ... perhaps returning to port with its catch. You pause to watch its progress ... observing a flock of gulls following in its wake ... silhouetted against the sky like moving scribbles of ink. It is as though the scene is unfolding just for you ... the gentle wind ... the scents and sound of the sea ... nature's wild beauty ... and you are filled with such appreciation for everything around you ... a deep sense of connection.

You travel on at a leisurely pace, seeing a flock of sheep grazing contentedly in a field ... hearing their occasional bleating carried on the air as you follow the path around the headland to where the track begins to slope downwards ... revealing a small sandy cove further ahead ... a place you have never seen before. This intrigues you and you quicken your pace ... just a little ... eager to discover what new delights lie before you on this lovely morning. The breeze is warmer now too ... the promise of a balmy day to come ... and you smile to yourself ... feeling so very relaxed ... so very calm. It is almost as though your feet are gliding along the narrow path now ... carrying you down and down so easily ... towards a flight of stone steps that descend to the beach. You stop for a moment at the top of the steps, one hand on the wooden rail that runs alongside them ... and glance down to the deserted cove ... edged by rocks both large and small. It looks inviting ... the curve of red-gold sand spread out before you ... smooth and untrodden ... all yours.

You start down the steps ... unhurriedly ... and when you reach the bottom, you slip off your shoes and leave them there ... allowing your bare feet to sink softly into the damp sand ... yielding beneath your toes as you stroll down to the sea. You anticipate the chill of the water but, as the surf bubbles over your feet, the sensation is pleasing ... refreshing. You study the vast expanse of steely blue ocean, stretching as far and wide as you can see.

The motion of the undulating waves is compelling somehow ... whispering over the shore ... before rolling back from where they came ... again and again ... over and over. You watch, spellbound ... feeling part of that eternal ebb and flow ... recognising how all your worries and cares are dispersing with each cycle ... until they are swept away ... completely dissolved ... leaving you calmed ... peaceful ... serene. As you splash along the shore now, you find yourself moving more freely ... your tread is lighter ... and your head is clear. You are refreshed and revitalised.

You understand that tides will always come and go ... sometimes calm ... sometimes wild ... and there may be storms ... but the sun will rise each morning ... just as it has today ... earth's natural rhythm ... and there are always new paths to be discovered ... nature's gifts to surprise you and lift your spirits. You raise your face up towards the sky that is now a tender blue ... opening your arms wide ... and luxuriate in the swell of joy that fills your senses.

At last, you turn and walk back up the beach to the steps, shaking the sand from beneath your feet and slipping them into your shoes once more. You climb up ... counting each step as you go ... from one up to ten. One ... two ... three ... four ... five. You pause halfway and look back at your beautiful secret cove ... noting how your footprints are already being erased by the incoming tide. But, like the tide, you know you can return here again and again ... just by following the path and taking those steps down to the shore. And as you count from five up to ten ... all the way up to the top of the steps ... you know that you are renewed and restored ... stronger and more resilient ... ready for whatever you need to accomplish.

Mini recharge meditation

This meditation allows you to take a few moments to step out of autopilot, to connect with yourself, so that you can refocus

Emma Last

Close your eyes and start to tune in to what is going on around you.

You are not stopping, you are only slowing down for a moment or two, so that you can connect with the present. You are giving your mind time and space. This will help you to become re-energised, more focused and productive.

You are noticing the sounds. You are observing what's happening without seeing.

What can you hear? What are the sounds that are closest to you? How many sounds or voices are there?

Bit by bit, start to tune into sounds that are further away. What can you hear? How many sounds or voices are there?

Start to bring your focus back in again, all the while scanning and listening for new sounds.

Once you have come back to you, you can start to open your eyes.

If you like, you can write down or discuss the sounds that you heard.

Rainbow dreams

A chakra balancing meditation to allow you to let go of worries
and recognise what is and isn't in your control

Sarah Bamber

Take a few gentle breaths here to settle your body … Now, take a moment to notice your breath … noticing the rise and fall of your chest and belly as you breathe easily and naturally … relaxing more and more with each breath, sinking into the bed or the chair or the floor with each gentle, relaxing breath.

Just use these few moments to notice where you are right now as we begin our journey …

Okay, now follow me as we begin our journey into the magical forest.

Imagine opening your eyes right now, look down to your feet and see a narrow path that stretches out ahead … on each side of the path are beautiful fields filled with wildflowers. Look around and take a moment to admire the vibrant colours of the flowers, the sapphire blue cornflowers … the vivid cherry-red poppies … the pink and white campions … the pretty faces of the tall, sturdy daisies looking up to the sun … look behind you and enjoy the view … the wildflower meadows stretch out as far as the eyes can see … As you look up, you can feel a whisper of a breeze on your face … the sky is so vast and blue, it reaches to infinity. There's hardly a cloud in the sky, it's a perfect summer's day and you feel your heart is filled with joy. Now, take a lovely deep relaxing breath in as you turn your attention back to the path ahead of you … there are no signs saying which way to go but you follow the path, you instinctively know the way, stepping forward as you breathe out … through the flowers, feeling them brushing against your legs and fingertips as you walk.

The path leads you through the flowers towards a beautiful forest … the trees are so tall and majestic … and, as you step nearer, you can hear the sounds of the leaves blowing gently in the breeze. As you draw nearer still, you notice the path leads you between two huge, noble oak trees, their beauty drawing you in. Reaching out, you touch the scaly bark of the trunk … feeling curious, you run your fingers between the fissures and feel a tingle in your fingertips as you absorb its towering strength. And, as you walk around its ancient girth, you look up under the mighty canopy; you can just about make out the blue sky and sunshine glinting way, way up through the treetops. Moving onwards, you feel the wisdom, the honour and protection of these mighty 'Kings of the Trees' surrounding you.

Looking ahead, you are struck by the fairy-tale-like beauty … the trees rise up from the mossy ground, their emerald-green tops stretch high up to the sky. The birds are singing their sweet, sweet songs of happiness and love … you watch them joyfully flitting from branch to branch, they are dazzling blues and yellows, the oranges and reds of their feathers are mesmerising as they dance on ahead.

In the distance, you hear water … following this sound, you reach a small waterfall … the water gently cascading into a stream below. Slowly, you begin to turn left, following the path. Again, there are no signs telling you which way to go; you are simply following your heart.

After a few more steps, the path takes you around a corner, and leads you to a wide-open space. In the middle of the clearing, the birdsong is becoming louder and louder, their excitement enthralling.

You are getting closer. A slow glance ahead bears unimaginable beauty and calmness. You have found it, the source of excitement … the reason for your journey.

Perfectly positioned right in the centre of the clearing, is a ginormous cherry blossom tree.

You can't help but make your way towards it … you walk forward, your arms outstretched with the sheer beauty of it all … you find yourself twirling and swirling around, taking in the wondrousness of it all … the serene beauty takes your breath away. You feel dwarfed by the sheer size of this magical tree.

As you reach the foot of the cherry blossom tree, you notice the base is encircled in lush green grass; perfect for sitting on. You pick a spot and slowly sit down, leaning back to gaze up at the underside of the canopy, seeing the small, delicate, perfect, pink flowers … the scent of lilac, rose and vanilla fills the air … it is almost too much to take in … you lie back on the soft grass, close your eyes and breathe in deeply … the cool air cleansing you, yet you feel it warming your soul.

After a few moments of peace and calm, you realise you have fallen asleep just for a few seconds … you feel like you are dreaming. You open your eyes and, as you look up, you notice that the perfect, pale pink flowers are now all the colours of the rainbow. You feel a gentle breeze starting to blow, the leaves of the surrounding trees start to rustle and wave in the breeze, and now, the blossom starts to fall, fluttering downwards.

First of all, vibrant red petals fall, gently floating down like confetti … you can hardly feel them as they land on you.

But as the thin layer of red petals starts to cover you, your whole body becomes energised and infused by the redness … with no resistance, you feel the petals absorbing your worries and fears … your breathing is slow and relaxed … and, as the breeze picks up again, it starts to gently blow away the red petals, taking these worries and fears with them as they float off into the distance.

After a moment, the blossom begins to fall again … this time they are a brilliant shade of orange. Orange allows you to experience joy and also release any shame and guilt. Feel the covering of orange petals absorbing these negative feelings … and as the breeze begins to blow, notice it taking away the shame and guilt, making more space for joy in your life …

Again, the blossom starts to fall … this time the petals are a bright yellow. Feel as the yellow petals gently land upon you and, as they cover your whole body, they begin to cleanse you of emotional pain … As you continue to rest here, you begin to realise that some things in life are out of your control and are best handled when you are calm and collected. Feel your body strengthen and become more secure, your mind is becoming much clearer … The breeze picks up the yellow petals now and they gently float away. Take a nice deep breath and feel the clarity within …

The next petals to fall are a vivid green, the likes of which you have never seen before … As they gently cover you, you feel them balancing and restoring your physical body. Green purifies the whole system, renewing your expression of love and forgiveness. Just as you love – you are loved. Feel these green petals open your heart to all the love you deserve. Know that you are connected to all that surrounds you as they gently blow away in the breeze …

Next to fall are beautiful, cooling, magical blue petals. These blue petals fall firstly on your throat before they cover you from head to toe … feel the magical blue petals enhancing your self-expression, allowing you to speak your truth. Feel the blue all around you, allowing you to express yourself, according to your true self. Breathe in and out freely as they gently blow away on the breeze.

This time it's the turn of the velvety indigo and purple petals. Feel them start to fall on your head and crown area before they land over the whole body. Indigo and purple stimulate your own healing power and wisdom, they increase your intuition and connection with others. Feel the calming influence of the velvety petals as they gently blow away on the breeze.

And finally, the petals turn to brilliant glowing white. As they fall, feel them embrace you, warm and pure. These heavenly white petals take away any pain and heal you of any hurt. It shows you the peace and joy within your own spirit. Take this moment to enjoy the whiteness that covers you, that surrounds you, that fills you, that holds you secure.

As you continue to lie here, enjoy how you feel, enjoy being yourself. Know that you are perfect. And as you rest under the whiteness, know that you are now cleansed inside and out, in body, mind and spirit. You are lying in complete peace and harmony, with yourself and the world, both physical and spiritual.

The gentle breeze has now carried away all the colours of the rainbow, taking with them your worries and fears, any shame or guilt, your emotional pains, stress and all tension and any physical pain.

You are now filled to the brim with peace and joy, with a clear and strong mind, a heart totally filled with all the love that you deserve, a voice that you are proud to express yourself with. You feel healed, full of a powerful wisdom, with a calm and free spirit, secure in the knowledge that you are perfect inside and out …

Taking one last look up to the blossom tree, you see it has once again become filled with delicate pink petals. As you raise yourself to sit once again, you breathe in deeply, the clean, enchanting air that this magical place has to offer filling your lungs, slowly breathing out and relaxing your body and mind.

After a short while, you carefully get to your feet, standing under the cherry blossom tree, feeling strong and tall. The beautiful birds return once more … chitter chattering to each other, darting and dancing in front of you, drawing your attention to another path. This path leads away from the magical cherry blossom tree, winding its way through the tall trees. You walk with a lightness in your step and sheer joy in your heart, feeling strong and secure, and blessed with all that you have just experienced.

As you continue along this path, you become aware of the beautiful bright light in the distance, shining through the canopy of the trees. Walking towards the light makes you thoughtful, and you ponder 'if one tree has so much power, how much power does a forest hold?' The distant light becomes closer and closer now, and soon you are stepping out into the sunlight and the wildflower meadows where we began our journey ...

Now it's time to return to reality, so let's start to become aware of your own surroundings, bringing your attention back to the room where you are right now, fidgeting a little on your chair or on your bed. Wiggling your fingers and toes. Breathe gently in and out and, when you are ready, slowly begin to open your eyes, giving them time to focus. Give yourself a chance to become fully present before carrying on with the rest of your day.

Reflection

A time for reflecting, switching off and recognising your needs

Emma Last

Close your eyes and start to tune in to your breathing. Put your hands on your diaphragm and start to feel the breath coming into your body, making sure that you can feel the rise and fall of your hands.

By focusing on your breathing, you are allowing your mind to calm and relax. Feel the weight of your body move closer to the ground as you relax.

Breathe in … and breathe out …

Breathe in … and breathe out …

Breathe in … and breathe out …

Start by connecting with the physical feelings in your body. What are you noticing?

You are slowing down, you are calming yourself, you are relaxing yourself.

Now to your feelings.

What are you noticing? In your mind, say, 'I am feeling … '

Let whatever feelings are in your head and body out. Breathe them out into the world. There are no good or bad feelings … you are not judging. You are only noticing your feelings …

What have you learnt from your feelings today?

Take your time … You are more relaxed.

You are taking the time to notice the present, to give yourself the space to reflect and relax.

Now to your needs. You have all the answers within.

Breathe in and feel the air fulfil one of your needs.

What do you need for your well-being?

What do you need to flourish?

What do you need to help you to switch off and/or to sleep well?

Take your time … you are calm and in control.

Listen to your needs. You are looking after your needs.

What one thing can you plan to do (tomorrow) to satisfy your needs?

What have you learnt about your needs today?

Take your time … You appreciate what you have learnt today. You are grateful.

What are you grateful for today?

What are you grateful that you have learnt about yourself today?

When you are ready to return to the present, open your eyes and start to take in your surroundings, holding onto those feelings of calm, relaxation and gratitude.

Once you have come back to you, you can start to open your eyes.

If you like, you can write down or discuss your feelings, needs, actions and things you are grateful for.

The cleansing waterfall

Transform your negative beliefs, feelings and thoughts by cleaning, clearing, releasing and re-energising in this magical healing waterfall

Maggie Matthews

I would like you to take a deep breath in and let it out slowly … then again, another deep breath in and release it out slowly … feeling yourself relaxing.

Adjust your position and get really comfortable and feel the calmness within … feel the tensions of the day just drifting away … as if you were on a boat being pushed out onto a gentle, rippling stream, where your hand is draped over the side of the boat, and you can feel the warm water with your fingertips being gently massaged in the water. Just floating gently along with the stream, with the sun warming your body, making you feel safe, warm and relaxed … listening to the water bouncing over the small rocks and feeling the boat being gently rocked with the rhythm of the water … listening to the birds in the trees and a gentle breeze softly on your skin, caressing and soothing you … feeling the tranquillity within you rising and spreading to every part of your body, into every pore and every cell, releasing all the stresses of the day and just letting go … just letting go … feeling yourself going deeper and deeper … and more relaxed into a gentle, relaxed, calm state, just as if you are drifting off into a gentle sleep. As you relax more and more, your body is getting heavier, and you go deeper and deeper into a state of deep relaxation … as you drift down the stream … enjoying the flow and the movement of the stream.

I am going to count down from ten to zero … as I count down, I would like you to imagine that you are stepping down out of the boat onto a wooden landing strip, or onto the grassy bank of the stream and walking down a small path, where you come to some trees, which fill you with calmness, peacefulness and tranquillity. With each step you take, you are coming closer to a beautiful waterfall, which you are going to step down into for cleansing and clearing ... releasing and re-energising. Just let your imagination guide you and feel yourself stepping down into this beautifully clear, sparkling waterfall surrounded by trees.

Ten: You are stepping down into calmness and relaxation ...
Nine: Going deeper and feeling more relaxed ...
Eight: No one wanting anything, no one demanding anything ...
Seven: Relaxing and going deeper now ...
Six: Calmer and calmer still ...
Five: Relaxing more and more ...
Four: Deeper and deeper ...
Three: Another step-down, down into tranquillity ...
Two: Deeper and deeper still ...
One: All the way down to calmness and peacefulness ...
Zero: Relaxing and going deeper ...

Relaxation washes all over you as you are now standing under a beautiful clear waterfall, where the sun's rays are coming through the water and you see a rainbow of beautiful colours transforming the water into a pool of healing light, which is cocooning you from head to toe. As the colours of the rainbow heal you, you feel an overwhelming sense of love ... coursing through your body, healing you, loving you and releasing anything that does not serve you from your past and present ... guiding you and protecting you ... transforming your negative beliefs, feelings, thoughts and emotions into positive and happy thoughts ... raising your confidence and self-esteem ... being at one with the universe. A feeling of oneness with Mother Nature and the beauty that surrounds you. A new feeling of self-worth and clarity, letting go of any old beliefs or behaviours that you have picked up along the way, on your life's journey. As you grow from strength to strength, you feel gratitude for this amazing experience that has freed you from the negativity that has been controlling you ... for you are now the master of your life, controlling your thoughts, feelings and emotions, becoming more confident and more positive … feeling inspired, stronger and more powerful … having a new direction, a new sense of belonging and achieving anything you want in the here and now. You are now the person you have always wanted to be; positive, confident, happy, peaceful and successful.

The fountain

A beautiful hypnosis script for deep relaxation promoting
a calm mind and body

Caroline Measures

Let's begin by settling right down, coming to rest in the present moment. If you're sitting, you can imagine you're sitting with a gently stacked spine that allows your body to relax while remaining alert throughout the meditation. It can be helpful to picture a fine silver thread running all the way up your spine, up out of the top of your head and all the way up to the universe above. Or you might be lying down comfortably on a bed or the floor, feeling safe and grounded. Whatever is right for you now. The important thing is to allow yourself this breathing space and just notice how you can become more aware of yourself and your immediate surroundings as everything slows right down. Even the air around you seems to settle now in response to you taking this time to get quiet and still.

You might become aware of some sounds wherever you are. See if you can notice them simply as sounds. Are they near or far, high-pitched or low, hard or soft? You can relax with sounds all around, just like the gentle breeze rustling the leaves on the trees or the soft swooshing of the waves as they flow back and forth on the seashore.

Your body might be feeling a little bit heavy now as you allow yourself to move deeper and deeper into relaxation. Feel the points of contact between your body and whatever you are sitting or lying on. Feeling held and supported. Safe and comfortable – able to go further down into rest and relaxation. With every breath you take, you can find yourself sinking more and more. So peaceful. So tranquil.

So still, that perhaps you can even feel your heart beating in your chest. Becoming aware of that constant background beat of life; constant, steady, reassuring. As your breath comes and goes all by itself. No need to change or control it in any way. Just allow it to flow, easily and effortlessly. The breath is your anchor to this moment. Maybe you become aware of the tiny pauses at the top of each in-breath and the bottom of each out-breath. Just noticing. And with each in-breath, you can say in your mind, "Calm", and on the out-breath, "Calm". Breathing in calm and breathing out calm. Breathing in calm and breathing out calm. Breathing in calm and breathing out calm …

I'd like you to imagine that you're standing at the top of a beautiful staircase made of glowing white marble. We are going to go down the staircase together, one step at a time. Stepping down, 1 … stepping down again, 2 … another step down, 3 … moving further down now, 4 … 5 … further and further down, 6 … 7 … deeper and deeper, 8 … 9 … and 10, stepping down into a magical garden full of colour and life.

Start walking along the grassy pathway that leads you through the flowers. Notice the bright colours in so many different shades around you. There are reds, pinks, blues and yellows, orange, white, purple and green. Breathe in the heavenly perfume as you stroll among the flowers. Some of them are taller than you, so you have to look up to see their heavy nodding heads. Some are carpeting the ground like a jewel-studded rug, sparkling and shining in the sun. And every other size in between. Look around and spot your favourites. Feel the warmth of the sun on your face as you walk deeper and deeper into the garden. The sky is blue, and the birds are singing in the nearby trees.

The fresh green grass is soft and springy underfoot. There are butterflies flitting all around in this beautiful, natural place and the bees are going about their business, humming happily as they visit flower after flower.

You can pause now and again to smell a bloom that catches your eye. Lean in to look more closely at the fragrant heads. Gently touch the leaves and petals and just notice the differences between them – some are soft and downy, others are waxy and cool, and all are perfect.

As you continue along the path, a warm breeze caresses your face. Make your way further and further into this wonderful garden and, with every step, you're feeling more and more relaxed and more and more at peace now.

You're nearly at the centre of the garden, where you become aware of the gentle sound of water. Tinkling softly like tiny fairy bells. There's an archway of flowers marking the entrance to the heart of this magical place.

Walk towards the archway and step through, feeling the cool grass underfoot and find yourself in a clearing where a huge sparkling crystal fountain stands in the middle. Sunlight dances off the water droplets, which glitter like diamonds and rainbows as they fall into the pure, clear pool below. This is a healing fountain, which will wash away any stress, any hurt, any sadness, any worries, leaving you refreshed, cleansed, lighter and completely at peace.

You can sit on the edge of the fountain and feel the soft spray on your skin. Lean over so you can see your reflection in the water and allow a gentle smile to lift the corners of your mouth. Smile at yourself! This place is so peaceful, and the water looks so inviting. It's as if the fountain has called you here for restoration on every level. You can leave your clothes on the grass and step into the pool around the fountain. The crystal-clear water is the perfect temperature for you. It's wide enough and deep enough for you to lie down and float, allowing the soft cascades to swirl around you.

As your body and mind relax more and more, the fountain slows to a trickle and then stops, so all you can hear is the occasional droplet, the sound of the birds singing in the trees and the gentle breeze through the leaves on the trees. Breathe in the fragrance of the nearby garden of flowers. Time stands still in this beautiful place. You can float suspended and completely at peace in the magical water. Allow the rainbows to fill and surround your body with their healing light, bringing peace and tranquillity, love and calm. Feel the warmth of the sun on your skin, giving you energy and vitality. Soak it all in and rest here for a while ...

(Pause for a few minutes.)

As you breathe in the natural perfection of this beautiful place, ever so slowly, a trickle of water starts to flow over the fountain again. Just a few drops at first, falling into the pool where you are floating. The sound is like tinkling bells, chiming beauty and peace all around you. Over the next few moments, the fountain slowly gains in strength until it is once again in full flow with a sparkling cascade into the pool. You belong here and this place resides deep within you.

In your own time, you can get up and out of the fountain, finding yourself completely dry and clothed when your feet touch the grass. The sun is shining, the birds are singing and the air is full of calm. You can thank the beautiful fountain for its healing powers of peace and love, and make your way back to the archway that leads into the garden. Take all the time you like. These feelings of deep relaxation will go with you, they are part of you.

Step through the archway into the colourful garden with its bright flowers of every shade you can imagine. There is so much abundance here, so much life and natural harmony. Follow the path back through the flowerbeds and smile at the beauty all around.

You come to the bottom of the white marble staircase. It glows with energy and reminds you that this magical place is here for you at all times. You just have to recall the flowers or fountain to find yourself transported into soothing, natural calm. Take a last look around the garden, feeling the sun on your skin, a gentle breeze against your face, and turn towards the marble steps.

We'll walk up the steps together, one at a time. Stepping up to the first one, 10 … and up again, 9 … moving up the steps, 8 … starting to become aware of your body again, 7 … coming up, 6 … noticing your breath, following it all the way in and all the way out, 5 … feeling more alert, 4 … as you step up, 3 … becoming aware of your surroundings, perhaps noticing sounds, movements, 2 … getting ready to open your eyes, 1 … opening your eyes and taking a nice stretch, feeling wide awake, refreshed and so, so relaxed.

The soul within

A powerful way to recover from ailments that began in childhood such as anxiety, hurt, lack of confidence, fears and much more

Norah Mahony

You are entering a state of deep relaxation … A place where your mind, body and soul are ready for total transformation …

You are here because you are ready to change things and make them work better for you. Often, things that cause us hurt and pain are carried from our childhood …

This may or may not be conscious to us …

But by connecting back to a time when we first began to feel these emotions, we can heal from our core level and make powerful changes in the now.

So, let's go and meet the younger you now … in your mind's eye, I want you to imagine you are standing outside a house …

You recognise the house from a time when you were small. Maybe it is your old home, your current home, or someone else's …

But you see that house now and you decide to take steps towards the house to meet your younger self …

You are feeling safe and confident. You know that you are an adult now and that you are safe and protected …

You are totally safe …

So, walk through the front door now and through the house until you find your younger you …

Maybe she is in the kitchen, or bedroom, or outside … you'll know when you find her …

You find the little girl …

You notice her sitting there and she notices you …

She smiles at you …

She looks sad … unhappy … What age is she?

…

She knows you are there for her …

She knows you love her …

She knows who you are. She feels safe and secure with you …

You go over to her and you wrap her into a deep, loving hug and she rests into you, feeling your love and safety all around her. You feel the tension in her little body relaxing into you now …

You ask her why she is crying …

Listen now to her reply … …

… …

She tells you somebody has upset her.

Who is that person?

…

What happened?

…

She tells you about her hurts – listen to the little girl deeply now for a few moments …

…

(Here you can integrate suggestions that the client may have told you in the consultation, using specific emotions, or experiences that have been shared with you.)

Let her tell you everything. There is all the time in the world.

… …

You notice as she speaks to you and trusts you and loves you that she is getting stronger as she lies in your arms.

Tell her she is safe now …

Tell her that you are sorry that she has to go through this and that, in fact, everything turns out more than all right in the end … Tell her all of the great things that are in your life now as an adult …

Tell her that you will walk with her always, she is not alone … She will never be alone again …

What else do you want to tell her … ? Speak with her now … tell her what she needs to hear …

And I want you to tell her this now – silently or out loud, you can repeat this:

I have prepared a special place for you.

You will be with me always and I will be with you.

From this day forward, you know and understand that you are not alone.

You will never be alone on this journey.

You are perfect.

I am here with you.

I am so glad you are this little girl.

I love being with you.

You are special.

The world smiled and gave thanks the day you were born.

You are magical.

There has never been another like you in this world and there never will be again.

Sometimes people treat others badly and you know that is their problem, not yours.

You are perfect, just the way you are.

I love you and you are not alone.

We will be together always.

… …

You notice the little girl knows the truth now. She is smiling. She understands … You hug her tight and she becomes one with you … watch her little body shine brightly as it becomes one with yours now … A beam of light flashes through your body and you feel immense peace, love and joy that you are fully connected in this space, right now, confident and strong and full of love. Both connected as one forever. Safe … peaceful … grateful.

You realise you have reclaimed that little girl. She will never be alone again.

You have a deep knowing now that you can accomplish anything. In the past, what you thought was holding you back was controllable by you.

You get to decide how your life plays out. And you decide that from this day forward you live your greatest life. You are a powerful, magical human being and you claim your place in this world right now.

When you are ready … you can begin to walk out of the house and out of the garden ... past your old school, past your teenage years, and into an adult memory of feeling huge love and feeling confident, wanted and safe.

Confident, powerful, secure, safe, loved ...

Let those feelings grow and fill you with those feelings and multiply it by ten ... and then a hundred ... feel yourself bursting with love and confidence and the realisation that can achieve anything you want to ... You can be and do anything you want to in this life ...

You are safe to succeed.

Woodlands restorative practice

A guided relaxation inviting you to explore a mystical autumnal
woodland to release, recharge and realign

Pamela Gilvear

This practice takes you on a nourishing and restorative autumnal walk
amongst woodlands, leaving you feeling relaxed, refreshed and recharged.

I would like you to imagine yourself standing on the edge of an inviting
woodland. It's a beautiful autumnal day. The sun is sharing its waning rays,
you feel the warmth on your skin. The coolness and the dampness in the air
is softened by the autumnal sun.

You are lovely and warm, wrapped up appropriately for this time of year
and you are curious to explore and experience the natural gifts this mystical
woodland has to offer.

The trees are still holding onto some of their leaves, with some having
been let go covering the path with a vibrancy of colour, crunching beneath
your feet as you start to walk into the woodland. There is an array of colours;
greens, yellows, oranges, golden russets, browns, which creates a warmth
and richness to the energy of the place.

You hear the gentle wind blowing intermittently through the leaves; in
between, there is palpable silence.

As you take some steps now walking into the woodland, you notice you
feel excited to be here and are curious to explore and experience the energy
of the place.

Take a few moments here to pause, using all your senses, to immerse
yourself fully into this woodland …

...

Take time to listen to the wind.

Notice how it feels as it gently whistles past your ears ...

...

Notice how gracefully the trees let go of their leaves, gently floating down to rest on the ground below, as the ecological tidying up process gets under way.

Nature showing how easily it is to let go, recycle and rebirth when we surrender and allow ...

...

Allow yourself to fully immerse and bathe in the autumnal colours of the woodland.

Experiencing the energy of the trees, notice how you feel as you look at their roots, trunks, branches and leaves. You may wish to sit amongst the roots, place your hands on the trunk, hug the tree. Do what you are intuitively drawn to do, what feels right for you ...

...

Imagine all that the tree has witnessed, how it naturally flows through each season, letting go in autumn, standing bare, hibernating, dormant in the winter months. In spring, buds appear, showing new growth, coming into bloom in the summer to its full potential. Standing firm and strong, deeply rooted to the earth throughout the changes of the seasons the years bring.

Feel the soothing, cleansing, replenishing energy of the mighty trees ...

...

Feel the soft warmth of the autumnal sun on your body, allowing it to bring feelings of comfort, softening releasing, letting go of any tension in the mind and body ...

...

Smell the woodland scents. There is woodsmoke in the distance, along with a mix of earthy, musky, sweet aromas of mushrooms, composts, earthy smells ...

...

Notice the sun's light dappling through the trees on to the ground. As the sun shines on the moss, it gives it an almost illuminous presence ...

...

You hear scurrying, movement from the woodland animals and birds.

You may see a squirrel, robin, deer, rabbit. What wildlife do you see? ...

...

As you stand in this woodland, take a moment now to turn your attention inward, into your body. Be curious, noticing how it feels as it experiences the restorative energy of this place.

Notice the sensations that are present for you in your body.

How do you feel?

What are you noticing?

You may notice tingling, heat, cold, shifting of energy, buzzing, energising, a sense of replenishment, peace, serenity, acceptance, love, calmness, a sense of nourishment. There is no right or wrong way to experience this.

Just observe, without judgement, how your body is responding to the natural gift of nourishment, recharging and replenishing from the woodland ...

...

Take some time now to walk through the woodland, using your instinct to guide you in the direction you need to walk. Know you are perfectly safe and held in the vibrant energy of this beautifully natural and nurturing environment.

You may choose to climb over the rotted tree that has fallen over in the last storm. If it's too big to climb over, there will be a gap underneath one of its branches you can easily crawl under.

Take in the energy of the woods as you get curious and explore all that nature has to offer. Notice how your body feels as you walk amongst the energy of the trees, along the many well-trodden paths. Or you may choose to go off the path and explore the denser foliage of the woods.

Use all your senses to connect with the wonderfully healing properties of this place.

As you look up, looking at the height of the trees as they stretch into and merge with the sky, notice the great strength and energy you feel as you soak in the trees' great presence. Take some time to pause here gazing towards the sky ...

...

I will leave you for a few minutes to explore the wonders of this space. I will call you back when it is time to regroup.

(Give the group a few minutes to explore for themselves.)

...

It is now time for you to walk towards the glow of a bonfire you can see in the distance.

You can see the smoke from the fire waft up into the sky and there is a sweet, earthy aroma of the logs burning.

Start to walk towards it, be aware of your pace, allow it to be slow and relaxed, there is no rush. If you rush, you will miss out on so much of the beauty around you and how you experience this felt sense in your body.

As you are drawn deeper and deeper into the woods towards the fire, you feel like the trees are hugging you, forming a warm protective blanket around you.

Notice how your body is responding as you get closer to the fire.

When you arrive, you notice there is a comfortable seat waiting for you in front of the fire.

Take your seat, taking your gaze to the fire – let the colours of the flames and the warmth of the fire soothe and comfort your mind, body and soul.

Allow the warmth and the energy of the fire to cleanse, heal, realign and recharge, restoring your mind, body and soul.

I will leave you here for a few minutes and call you back when it is time to return.

...

It is now time to take a last look around, absorbing the restorative energy of this place, knowing you can return at any time.

It is now time to leave the woodland; before you do, I invite you to go within and ask your body how it feels?

How is your energy feeling?

What are your energy levels?

What level is your battery icon showing?

Just notice without judgment ...

...

When you are ready, slowly and gently start to bring your awareness back to where you are in the room with me.

Become aware of the sounds around you in the room, have an awareness of the floor, walls, room size. Allow your body to stretch in whatever way is needed.

It can feel helpful at this point to take a slightly deeper breath in and, when you are ready, very gently open your eyes.

If time permits, you may wish to invite individuals to share their experiences; this can help them understand their own personal experience of the practice. Remind them there is no right or wrong way to have experienced it. Reassure them that whatever they experienced was perfect for them.

CHAPTER FIVE

Hypnobirthing

A stroll through the seasons

A hypnotherapy relaxation originally written for mothers who knew they would be giving birth to stillborn babies, but also used frequently and with success with viable pregnancies too.

Tania Taylor

Allow yourself to get into the most comfortable position for you now, being aware of your breath, not changing it, just noticing the breath. Be aware of the surface you are getting yourself comfortable on … aware of the music … and if you hear any other noise during our session today, you can acknowledge it, and simply let it go, bringing your awareness back to the sound of my voice whenever you notice your mind drifting with your own thoughts and dreams.

We are going to start by relaxing all of the muscles in the body, beginning with the head and face, the neck, shoulders, the arms, relaxing the torso, the legs. *(Here you specify each muscle in turn and you can include as few or as many as you want, dependent on how long you want your session to run, and depending on how relaxed you want your client to be by the time they get to the next section.)*

And, as you're relaxing there, I just want you to think of a colour, a colour that makes you feel calm, a colour that brings you comfort and strength, and just imagine for a moment that this colour is gently sweeping over your entire body, allowing you to feel calm, comfortable and in control … And you know that any time you think of this wonderfully calming colour enveloping your body, you will be safe, calm, comfortable … in control, and you can use this colour any time you wish ... throughout our session today ... throughout your days in the outside world ... continuing to imagine this colour now surrounding you, enveloping you ... a force within you that brings you strength and comfort ...

Really notice your whole body feel as comfortable and calm as you could possibly feel right now ... and ... as you enjoy these moments of calm that are just for you ... I'd like you to imagine that it is a beautiful autumn day, and you are standing at the top of ten elegant steps that lead you down into a forest, and just before the forest is the most wonderful, tranquil lake that you have ever seen, surrounded by a woodland of trees that appear to stretch out for miles ahead of you, a sea of warm yellows, browns, oranges and reds ...

And when you look at these steps, you know, you just absolutely know ... that each step you take ... will take you down into the most wonderful feeling of calm ... so, as I count down from ten to zero, you will notice yourself drifting deeper and deeper ... remaining aware of my voice, as you make your way down into this beautiful forest that creates a sense of calm, peaceful tranquillity.

10, stepping down so easily,

9, already noticing your breath becoming slower and steadier,

8, feeling calmer,

7, more at ease,

6, wondering what you might find in this beautiful place,

5, halfway there now, feeling more and more comfortable,

4, your body feeling lighter and lighter,

3, more relaxed now,

2, so light now, feeling as if you are just floating down to ...

1, perfectly at ease now as you take the final step to

Zero ... relaxing all the muscles in your body, feeling as perfectly tranquil as you could ever wish to, as you step forward towards the most beautiful lake.

A lake surrounded by trees with leaves filled with all the beautiful colours of autumn. You take a moment to get yourself comfortable by the lake, sitting down and just watching as leaf, after leaf, after leaf, gently ... slowly ... floats down onto the surface of the lake ... feeling more and more relaxed as each leaf floats gently down ... you see yellows, browns ... oranges and reds ... as each leaf gently falls to the lake ... and you just notice their shape, their size, notice the ripples that float in rings as each leaf touches the water in turn.

And your body continues to feel so light, like you could float along the path that leads you deeper into the forest. Floating past trees that have ripening fruits, some fruits are fuller than others, and each tree around you contains different colours of fruits. Some fruits have fallen to the floor too soon, others perfectly ripe, and others are still there, waiting for their calling. For the time when it is their turn to be ready for the autumn harvest.

And as you continue walking through the park, you feel so light, it's almost as if you are walking on white, fluffy, marshmallow clouds … in this wonderful dream, this place that is here all for you right now … a place where you can feel just as relaxed as you could ever imagine … and as you continue … the white clouds turn to frost and snow, you pay more attention to your surroundings and you can see that the trees have lost all their leaves now, and yet you know that this is a beautiful natural cycle … you know that this period of darkness will be temporary … you look up into the night sky and see stars gently flickering above … they feel soothing … and give out hope … because without the darkness, the stars could not shine so bright, or illuminate the sky in such a wonderous way … the frost and the snow create a magical wonderland ahead … enabling you to see the beauty throughout these cooler times … and as daylight returns … you look in awe … as the snow sparkles and shines … maybe you even notice a robin red breast perching on a snowy branch …

And as you continue to float on through this beautiful woodland … you notice a gap in the trees … where a bright beam of yellow, warm, sunlight is shining through … As the light gets closer, you feel yourself becoming warmed by the light, not too hot, just nice and comfortable for you … and you find yourself in a beautiful clearing … You can see a clear blue sky above you … you can hear the delicate sounds of bird song … and you feel a flow of real inner strength that flows through you and radiates from your every pore as you realise that spring is here … … you make yourself comfortable next to a small, still pond … really paying attention to all of the springtime sounds of the forest … taking in the natural beauty that surrounds you … The trees are covered in cherry blossom that is soon to be released gently from their branches …

You feel so relaxed here, in this wonderfully safe place … breathing … relaxing, with each surge just as you would hope to, each inhale surrounding you with calm … peace … tranquillity … each exhale surrounding you with calm ... peace ... tranquillity ... your body doing exactly what it was designed to do ... in the calmest ... most relaxed of ways ... and you know that our bodies are just like any other mammal ... and that we were made to blossom and birth in the same way as any other mammal ... as that stunning delightful mammal that gave birth in the woodland glade yesterday ... so peacefully ... so perfectly at ease ... because she knew what was going to happen ... just like you ... feeling so relaxed there ... know what is going to happen ... and this allows you to feel more and more confident, more and more capable ... as you continue with those natural breaths, allowing all fear to slide away ... We move further and further away from anxiety when we understand that what causes us anxiety ... is the fear itself ... and once we understand ... we do not accept anxious feelings anymore ... in fact ... we expel and let go of anything which is unhelpful to us ... breathing in, and enabling only warm thoughts and wonderful feelings ... to nurture and become ... part of your gentle experience here ... in this moment ... feeling so tranquil ... so calm ... comfortable ... and in control ... in this beautiful woodland glade ...

And before you move on from the calm, still, pond ... you stand and look into the water ... seeing your reflection gazing back at you ... and you notice something, you're not entirely certain what it could be, but you notice that something is different ... maybe your inner power is shining through? ... Maybe there is a determination, or peace, or calmness that wasn't quite there before? ... A confidence in yourself and how you will continue on through this journey of life, and this leaves you feeling inspired and capable, as you turn and move on, continuing through the woodland trail that is layered with a delicate carpet of flowered blossom petals ...

And, as you follow this footpath, you come to an opening ... ... you realise you have come to the end of your journey through the forest ... and you look out, at the most wonderful garden, you can see it forming right before your eyes, as green stalks of all different lengths grow, and flower, from seeds laid long ago ... growing in places they grew before ... With each new flower, comes the most wonderful of scents ... you walk around the garden, watching it grow as much as it can for now ... seeing all the colours of the rainbow ... bending down, you touch the occasional petal that catches your eye ...

And eventually, you come full circle, and look back at the forest behind you, the trees are green ... and you take a moment to realise just how far you have come … how much strength and trust you have gained on this stroll through the seasons … You look ahead at the sea of colours before you, and consider the colours you have seen on your journey today … yellows … browns … oranges … and reds … … darkness and light … whites … pinks … … and all the colours of the rainbow …

And you know that seasons will continue to change as the months pass … and that you can allow yourself to be carried by the seasons … allowing in darkness … and light … whenever you wish … knowing that you can envelop yourself in your safe colour whenever you want to … enabling you to feel safe … calm … comfortable … and in control … wherever you are … and for as long as you wish.

CHAPTER SIX

Instilling confidence

Finding calmness from within

This visualisation allows you to calm your nerves and/or anxiety and allows you to perform at your best. A useful tool when you have a big meeting, presentation or are trying something outside of your comfort zone.

Emma Last

We're now going to go and find your calm and safe place. somewhere where you won't be interrupted, where you can purely focus on you. Push your thumb against your first finger as if you are holding a small key in your hand. This is the key that will unlock the thoughts to your safe place.

Think about a place where you feel most relaxed and calm. It can be an imaginary place or a place you have been to in real life, a place where you feel peace and calm. Where would you like to go back to? Where helps you to feel calm? Where have you been your happiest? Where are you most relaxed but not sleepy?

You might envisage somewhere big or somewhere small, somewhere indoors or somewhere outdoors. The place might be a beach, a favourite spot on a walk you have been on, your garden, or a holiday you've been on, or it could be your imaginary place.

Decide on your place and start to create the vision of it in your mind.

Take your time …

Now start to tap into your senses.

What can you see in your calm place? Are there any flowers, trees or sea? Are there any buildings? Is there any water?

Take in your surroundings, breathe in every detail …

Are you alone in your place or are there others with you? Who is with you? Are there any animals or pets with you? If you have anyone with you, what are they doing? What do they look like? What age are they?

Take your time … Breathe in every little detail …

What calming sounds can you hear? Are there birds singing? Is there music playing? Or can you hear sounds from those who are with you? What are they saying? Is there a particular sound that is helping you to relax and feel at peace such as the sea lapping or trees swaying in the wind?

How do these sounds make you feel?

Take your time … Breathe in and grow the clarity of your image …

Think about the smells. Is there a scent of flowers? Or of cooking or baking?

Now consider all the things that you can touch. What can you feel in your calm place? Is it hot, breezy or cold? Can you feel the ground, sand or grass under your feet? Or can you feel the chair beneath your bottom? Is the sun shining on you? Can you feel the warmth of the sun on your skin? Or are there rain drops that you can put out your hands and touch? Are there things you can touch with your hands? Like water, sand, soil, trees or animals? How do the things you can touch make you feel?

Finally, is there anything you can taste? Have you already eaten something? Is there a taste in your mouth? What does it taste like? Are you tempted by any foods in your safe place? What would it taste like? How does it make you feel?

Take your time … Breathe in, take in every detail and grow the vision of your calm place in your mind.

Now let's revisit what you can see. What's in front of you? Look to both sides of you. If others are with you, what are they doing now? What are they wearing?

What colours and shapes can you see?

What are the things that you can see that make it your calm and happy place? What do you find most beautiful about your place that makes you want to keep coming back? What feelings do you have about your calm, safe and happy place?

Next to gain clarity on where exactly you are in your vision.

What is your age? What can you see yourself doing? What is it that you love doing in your happy, calm and safe place? You may be sitting, enjoying your place, relaxing, reading a book, walking or even doing a variety of things.

You have no worries, cares or stress. Feel those feelings of peace and happiness … feel how relaxed and calm and happy and re-energised you feel right now in your place. You're feeling completely and utterly at one.

Take your time … Breathe in, take in every detail. You want to remember the image and your feelings of calm and happiness in your safe place.

Know that you can return to your safe place whenever you need to.

Before you say goodbye to your safe place, push your thumb against your first finger, holding your imaginary key in your hand. Remember, this is the key that will unlock the thoughts to your safe place. Take a photo in your mind that you can return to when you need to feel calm and all you will have to do is squeeze your thumb against your first finger. Picture yourself in your calm, happy and safe place so that you can return to this image the next time. Store the image in a safe place in your mind, ready for when you need it.

When you are ready to return back to the present, open your eyes and start to take in your surroundings. Hold onto those feelings of calm and happiness as you return to your day.

You can repeat this visualisation at any time until you feel you have a strong image in your mind. Once you have the image you can use your thumb and first finger to anchor yourself back to your safe place. Once practised, your image should enable you to jump very quickly and easily to your safe place, which should allow you to calm yourself within a matter of minutes.

Revisiting your visualisation when you need to calm yourself

Push your thumb against your first finger and hold the imaginary small key – just the same as you did in the first visualisation. Think about the photo of your safe place – pull back to the photo image that you stored safely in your mind. Picture yourself in the image and start to get back to feeling all the feelings and visualising all the things that bring you calm, happiness and relaxation in your safe place.

Remember who was with you, what you were doing, what you saw, heard, smelt, touched and tasted and how calm it made you feel.

Breathe in every little detail … and feel how relaxed, calm and happy you feel in your safe place.

Savour the feelings of calm.

Push your thumb against your first finger, holding your imaginary key in your hand. Remember, with your key, you can return any time. Make sure you take a photo in your mind and picture yourself in your calm, happy and safe place so that you can return to this image the next time.

Open your eyes and start to take in your surroundings, holding onto those feelings of calm and happiness as you carry on with your day.

Hypnotic induction

Get into a deep state of trance using breath work and giving your conscious mind permission to switch off

Norah Mahony

As you feel your eyes closing …

Allow your mind to think about relaxing …

Let your imagination go over all the scenarios you would love to relax in …

Scenarios and places where there are no barriers or controls that limit your desires …

Your arms and legs are uncrossed, easily relaxed, heavy and happy to lie here with nothing to do for a change … here in this special place … as you give permission to relax and sink into relaxation …

You feel gravity pulling your body down into a deep muscle relaxation …

Your body relaxes … your shoulders … spine … arms … and legs … they relax deep down … your muscles are limp and loose as your mind clears and expands, ready for the suggestions you will receive … …

You are drifting into a space where desires can easily become a reality … where your breath slows down …

A space that will nurture your personal growth … and change your reality …

Begin to monitor your breath more closely now …

Take in some deep breaths. Slowly in through your nose and, even slower, you exhale through your mouth …

This simple act of air in and out of your body, slowly with rhythm, makes you even more still and peaceful …

On your own initiative, decide to hold your next breath gently …

You hold it carefully, without strain … the release takes longer to exhale than the hold …

Oxygen fills you up again … allowing your breathing to slow and move towards trance state …

Again, you decide to hold your next breath …

Carefully and gently, you hold it, enjoying how it fills out your ribs and lower diaphragm …

With a long, slow exhale, you breathe out. Twice as long as you held the breath … letting go of any negative thoughts or to do lists that have been gathering in your mind up until today …

Your ribs, lungs and diaphragm empty as oxygen floods your veins …

As the good air rushes in, feel the vibrancy and positivity … and breathe out the tension … all the way out …

Breathe in positivity and light … that's right … and breathing out those negative energies, thoughts or feelings … right now …

See the negativity or mind chatter that may still be taking up space in your mind now … see it like a dull cloud … that you are ready to let go of … see it receding from your outer physical body now … leaving the room or space you are relaxing in … Watch it go … that dull cloud … moving further and further away from you in every moment … bringing all the negativity and chatter with it for now.

You simply let go of it … shoulders and jaw relaxed … just watch it go … You notice your whole internal being glow brighter, feel lighter, more relaxed …

As you drift deeper … lighter … softer … relaxed …

It flows away from you for good now … let it go … see it go … notice now how it is gone … and how light you feel …

With each out breath, your body sinks further and further down …

Now in your mind's eye, you can connect with joy and peace so easily … as you imagine your favourite places that bring you to that level …

Enjoy that relaxing and letting go feeling …

Far from the business of everyday life … Relaxed …

Right here … where only love exists … you feel it expanding your relaxed and peaceful frame … see the bright light expanding throughout your body now …

The only barrier to your total peace and relaxation is you … if you will allow it to happen or not … Agree to let it happen and so it will be … Relax …

And you can nod your head to give full permission to your body to relax

... allow that relaxation to totally take over your body ... as you sink further and further down into the space beneath you ...

Into a space where you can feed your mind the future that you intend ...

Enjoy the heaviness of your eyelids now, softly closed, yet feeling like they are glued shut, locked together ...

You can try and open them if you like; notice how they stayed glued together, they don't open. They won't open. You can relax them again, allowing the softness to take over your eyelids and your whole body ... as you go deeper and deeper into relaxation, sinking down ... deeper than ever before.

You notice your breath ... this amazing action that we appreciate too little ... this unconscious activity that breathes life and vitality into us ... we never force our breath, it just happens ...

And just like the breath ... our subconscious mind does lots of other things for us too, without us even thinking about it ... our habits ... our mindset ... the things engrained in us ... and we need the subconscious to change any habits successfully ... hypnosis helps you to access the subconscious easily ... which is why you are here today ...

So you can relax and let it happen ... knowing you are fully aware the whole time ... totally relaxed ... and aware ... no need to think ... just follow my voice ... your body pulled down in relaxation ... you release any remaining hold on your muscles now ...

You feel the slightly cooler air entering your nostrils, followed a little later by the warm air of your exhale ...

Take pleasure in feeling your mind relaxing and letting go now ...

Any sounds you hear from the outside world only help to take you deeper and deeper ...

In fact, the noise of the outside world accompanies you, down and down, deeper and deeper ...

Into a place of deep relaxation, where transformations and manifestations are just normal ...

Where time and space collapse, where desires simply take shape, becoming part of us ...

And hypnotic trance is possible ...

Where you can reprogramme your mind, with full control and deeply relaxed ...

And did you know that making change in your life is so simple through hypnosis ... ?

All you need to do is believe what I say to be true and so it will be ...

Change through hypnosis is as easy as that ...

It is wanting something in your life to change ...

And allowing your body to relax and accept the suggestions of change that I give you ...

Sink down deeper into the couch/chair ... and relax now, deeper and more relaxed than ever before ...

Becoming much more comfortable than ever before ...

Feeling completely at peace ...

And calm and relaxed and contented ...

Your limbs are totally relaxed, gravity pulling them down ...

Drop down your shoulders, deeper and deeper ...

You are aware of warm blood pumping in rhythm with your calm heartbeat ...

Your mind is ready for change, ready to accept the future version of you who has everything ...

The version of you that has success in all areas of his/her life ...

Nothing can stop you now ...

There's nothing hindering you and no obstacles left to stop you from entering your healing trance ...

Be aware of this special time where you are allowing the space and time to allow hypnosis to happen ...

Look into the dark behind your eyelids as you acknowledge how willing and happy to go into hypnosis you are ... this beautiful time and space, created just for you ... here and now ... deeply relaxed ... relaxed and ready ... totally let go now ...

You feel totally at peace and in alignment with your body, mind and soul ... that's it ...

Yes, entering hypnosis is easy ...

You simply release your conscious mind from duty for a little while through relaxation to make this happen ... Your conscious mind is that beautiful small part of your mind that works so hard for you every day. That makes decisions and takes note of the day-to-day actions ...

Give permission now for that part of your mind to take a rest as you envision your subconscious opening fully up now to the suggestions that it will receive so change can come easily ... Unblocked and ready for change ... In this space of deep hypnosis ...

I am confidence

A guided relaxation which builds confidence and self-belief
and includes positive affirmations

Anne Gregory

It is often easier to relax when you sit down or lie down … because taking the weight off your feet helps you to relax … doesn't it? … …

You will find it easy to relax when you count from 10 … 9 … 8 … 7 … 6 … …

Which means that when you get to 5 … …

You are already halfway relaxed, are you not? … 4 … 3 … 2 … 1 … …

Notice how easily you allowed yourself to settle … and relax … you are a natural … …

And let go … just let go … of any physical tensions you may be able to feel in your body … …

Let go … of any tightness you may feel caused by emotional stress … …

Allow yourself to let go of any negative thoughts or ideas or feelings or beliefs you may have … …

And prepare for a massage of the mind … …

Just as your body knows how to relax and knows when to say no … so your mind hears when it is time to relax here … …

As soon as you give yourself permission to be calm … you are allowing yourself to find the balance within … until … eventually … you find you are completely centred … …

You may experience a wonderful feeling of well-being … …

I can see this is something you want to improve, is it not? ... ...

I would not tell you it is necessary because I know you already know the benefits of doing this ... ...

I know that you want to learn a different way to be, do you not? ... ...

Some people are able to feel calm and confident when they are in new situations ... by simply focusing on relaxation ... ...

You can feel confident in all situations ... ...

And you can choose to feel a little confident ... or very confident ... ...

I know you have felt confidence before ... have you not? ... have you ever thought about those times when you felt completely confident? ... ...

Can you think of those times now? ... ...

Perhaps it was a particular time in your life ... ...

Perhaps it was when you were doing a particular activity ... ...

Imagine if you could bring that feeling into your mind now ... ...

Feel those feelings again ... ...

Savour that confident moment ... ...

I am not sure how you will generate that confidence but it can happen ... all by itself ... very naturally ... until you realise how confident you feel ... both during this session ... and way ... way beyond ... ...

What is it like when you completely embrace that confident feeling? ... ...

When you think about confidence ... your body and your mind start to have the experience ... ...

I know you want to make that change ... you want to make that change ... and you can ... ...

You can change anything you want to change ... ...

To create something more beneficial for you ... you just need to decide ... ...

You just need to decide to change your mind ... because no one minds ... if you change your mind ... ...

Will you be changing your mind now or later? ... ...

You can complete this puzzle ... ...

And how will you know when you are completely confident ... and calm ... and comfortable? ... ...

You will know ... when all of your capabilities come to the fore ... when your competence shines through ... ...

You might like to imagine that now ... imagine your natural abilities shining like the sun ... radiating your brilliance outwards ... creating a force field around you ...

Suppose you could feel more confident ... simply by believing that you are ... ...

And ... suppose ... the more you believed it ... the more true it became ... ...

As you focus on your capacities ... you become even stronger in your belief that you can conquer anything at all ... you can achieve anything at all ... ...

As humans ... we can learn to interact confidently with other people ... and enjoy the interaction ... ...

As you find yourself practising ... you will notice how easily the conversation develops ... and how engrossed you become ... and how confident you feel ... ...

Think about a confident conversation ... and get a sense of that now ... ...

The more you engage in conversations ... the more proficient a communicator you will become ... ...

Will you begin now ... or at your earliest opportunity? ... maybe today? ... or maybe tomorrow? ... ...

You do not have to think about it ... you could just do it ... ...

Focus on how it feels to be comfortable and confident ... ...

What else do you notice? ... ...

Maybe you have not started to believe it yet ... there is plenty of time for you to do so ... ...

You could begin to believe it at any time ... ...

I could tell you that you should start to believe it immediately ... but you already know that ... ...

You do not have to ... (name) ... understand just how easy this process is ... ...

Have you realised that you are gaining a deeper knowledge about yourself ... and your innate abilities? ...

You can come to this new understanding ... because you have unlimited potential ... ...

You can be anything you choose to be ... ...

As you say to yourself ... ...

I am confident ... ...

I am certain ... ...
I am secure ... ...
I am self-assured ... ...
I am positive ... ...
I am poised ... ...
I am bold ... ...
I am bright ... ...
I am courageous ...
I am cool ... calm ... collected ... ...
I am decisive ... ...
I am determined to succeed ... ...

I feel confident in everything I do ... I open myself up to all the possibilities ahead ... as I continue to learn ... and develop ... and grow ... ...

I am sure of my abilities ... ...
I have creative ideas ... which I want to share ... ...
I am a confident speaker ...
I accept myself ... I trust myself ... I love myself ... ...
I am in control of my life and my destiny ... ...
I believe in my ability to succeed ... ...
I believe in myself ... ...

Life is a journey

A metaphor about the journey of life and how to overcome any
obstacles to achieve your goals

Anne Gregory

I am going to ask you to make yourself comfortable … take a nice deep
breath in … and … as you breathe out … relax and close your eyes … …

Breathe in … and hold … and breathe out … expelling the tensions of
the day with that breath … …

Breathe in … as you imagine calmness spreading throughout your body
… and then … breathe out … any stress you may be feeling … …

I would like you to think of this session as a tonic for your mind …
…

Maybe you already know how to relax … …

You can give yourself permission … now … to be calm … …

Tune in to your body … and find the balance within … …

Have you ever thought of your life as being a journey? … …

With any journey … there are often stops and starts … many different
modes of transport … a variety of paths to take … …

There can be hills and valleys … companions who join you along the
route and also times of solo travel … …

There can be changes of direction … sunrises and sunsets to see …
places to visit … some places you may wish to linger in and some places you
may simply pass through … …

At times … the distance between stops can be short … and sometimes
there is a long road ahead … …

Sometimes the road is straight and at other times it contains lots of twists and turns ... ...

The variety of the journey can keep you entertained and keep you wanting to move forward ... ...

Sometimes you can slow right down and really admire the views around you ... and sometimes you are in more of a rush ... ...

And everyone's journey is different ... ...

No two paths are exactly the same ... ...

And if you choose a path ... and ... after a short distance along it ... you realise it is not taking you where you want to go ... you can change it ... ...

There is no right or wrong way ... just the path that is right for you ... ...

And sometimes it is appropriate to meander and take in the sights and the sounds and the smells of a new place ... absorb the warmth of the sun on your skin ... or the smell of the pine trees ... and enjoy exploring and discovering new things and new people ... ...

And sometimes you want a more direct path to your destination ... ...

You may wonder if there is an aid to help you get there more quickly ... ...

Something similar to a sat nav ... ...

You know from journeys you may have been on before ... that a sat nav can take you where you want to go in the quickest ... or the shortest ... time possible ... ...

When you are very clear on your destination ... ...

By inputting a postcode ... or a street name ... into the device ... it knows exactly where you want to go ... because you have programmed it ... ...

And it can calculate the most beneficial route to take ... based on the volume of traffic ... or the weather conditions ... or the time of day ... ...

And do you know that your mind works in a similar way to the sat nav? ... ...

You really do have your own internal sat nav ... ...

And when it is programmed with the correct information ... it can help you to reach your destination ... it can speed up your journey to your next ... your desired destination ... and help you achieve your goals ... ...

By being very clear about what you want ... and by using the power of positive visualisation ... to embed the things you want into your mind ... ...

You can tap into ... and utilise ... your inner strengths ... your inner skills ... your natural abilities ... ...

To propel yourself forward … towards the things you truly desire … …

Keeping you focused on the things you want … not on what you do *not* want … but on the things you *do* want … …

And imagine yourself in that place … imagine yourself being that person … imagine yourself having achieved that goal … …

Remember … your brain cannot tell the difference between what is real and what is imagined … so … simply by imagining those things you truly want … your mind will believe that you already are that person who has those things … …

And every time you imagine it … you strengthen that idea … you give yourself … another inner rehearsal … you bring that goal closer to you … …

Your wonderful mind will work very hard … to help you to make this vision become a reality … in the quickest possible time … just like your very own sat nav! … …

So spend some time now … thinking about what you want … …

Is it more confidence … is it more calm in your life … is it more control over situations? … …

Your perception of your situation is already changing … isn't it? …

Your perception of your abilities is changing too … …

Would you like a new job … do you want a new house … are you looking for a new partner? … …

Take your time … …

There may be a few ideas in your mind … …

Allow your mind to settle on one … …

Allow your mind to settle on the thing you want to focus on at this time … …

Think about it … …

Create an image in your mind … …

Or a visualisation … …

Or a phrase … …

Or a colour … …

Or anything else that illustrates this one thing for you … …

And now focus on it … …

Or expand it in the eye of your mind … if you want to … …

See the image … …

Are there any sounds associated with it? … …

What can you feel? … …

How do you feel? ... ...

If you allow your mind to clear ... then you can relax into this beautiful daydream ... ...

If you want to ... you can bring that daydream to life now ... ...

You are able to create the life of your dreams ... and your daydreams ... ...

You can see yourself living that new life ... can you not? ... ...

A person may choose this new path in life ... believing this is the right path to take ... and the right time to take it ... ...

I am wondering if you know how wonderful you will feel ... having given yourself permission to explore this new path ... ...

You can continue to discover the opportunities awaiting you ... should you choose to take this new direction ... ...

Notice ... with each step along the path ... you feel more and more relaxed ...

You can take great satisfaction in your progress ... one step at a time ... there is no rush ... you can do this at your own pace ... in your own time ... I know you are thinking about it ... ...

And now you can enjoy it even more ... ...

Knowing it is the right thing to put yourself first ... to do what is right for you ... as you say to yourself ... this is my chosen path ... and I deserve the best ... ...

Manifest your goals

Manifest and achieve your goals using visualisation

Emma Last

When you are ready, close your eyes. Let the weight of your body ground with the space that you are sitting or lying on and start to let any tension float out of your body. Start by breathing deeply into your heart and deeper into your abdomen, hold for a couple of seconds and breathe out. Slowly push the breath out of your body. Repeat until you feel safe and relaxed.

Now deepen your relaxation by using square breathing:

Breathe in for 4 … 1, 2, 3, 4

Hold for 4 … 1, 2, 3, 4

Breathe out for 4 … 1, 2, 3, 4

Hold for 4 … 1, 2, 3, 4

Make sure that the breaths that you are breathing out are as focused and important as the breaths that you are breathing in.

Take a moment to notice and feel the sense of stillness within your body.

Think of the goal that you want to achieve. You may want to envisage a big goal or something smaller, something that is important to your happiness or something that is going to be a measure of your success.

Decide on your goal and start to create the vision of it in your mind.

Take your time …

Your image is going to become as clear as a photo in your mind. Start to form the image. Tune in your focus on the image. Take your time … your aim should be to pick up on every detail. You want to see its colours in full definition. You are going to make your image become a reality.

Reach out your arm in front of you – you are in reaching distance of your goal.

To truly connect with your goal, start to think about what your goal will mean to you when you achieve it.

Think about what you see yourself doing when you reach your goal. Take your time ... Take in the details of this image. Where are you? What are you doing? Do you notice anything about yourself? Are you alone or are there others with you? How does seeing this image make you feel?

Breathe in every little detail ...

What sounds can you hear? How do these sounds make you feel?

Take your time ... Breathe in and grow the clarity of your image ...

Are there any smells that you notice, or do you have a taste in your mouth that helps you to cement your image and feelings of achieving your goal?

Earlier, you reached out within touching distance of your goal; now you've achieved it, you can touch it. What are the things that you can touch? What can you feel under your feet? If you are seated, what can you feel under you? What can you feel on your body or face? Are there things you can touch with your hands? How does touching what you have achieved make you feel?

Take your time ... Breathe in, take in every detail and grow the vision of the goal you have achieved in your mind.

Take your time ...

Now let's revisit what you can see. What different things do you see when you look through your new eyes and feel this? Your new reality. What's in front of you? Look to both sides of you. How do you appear? What are the things that you can see that make your goal and vision a reality?

How does achieving your goal make you feel? How do you feel physically? How do you feel mentally? What emotions do you feel now you have achieved your goal? What do you notice that is different about you?

Achieving your goal fills you with joy, happiness and gratefulness. You are calm and in control. You have abundance. You feel fulfilled. You are proud of your confidence and ability to achieve your goal.

Take your time ... Breathe in, take in every detail. You want to remember the image and your feelings of calm and happiness in your safe place.

Know that you can return to your safe place whenever you need to.

Before you say goodbye to your safe place, reach out your arm in front of you. As you reach out and touch your goal, take a photo in your mind, a high definition, full-colour and crystal clear image that you can return to when you need to reaffirm your goal or vision. Picture yourself in the image, being fully present – it is your current reality. You can return to this image the next time. Store the image in a safe place in your mind, ready for when you need it.

When you are ready to return back to the present, open your eyes and start to take in your surroundings, holding onto those feelings of joy, happiness and abundance. You feel fulfilled as you return to your day.

You can repeat this visualisation at any time until you feel you have a strong image in your mind. Once you have the image you can use your arm to anchor yourself back to the vision of your goal.

Revisiting your visualisation

When you feel you need to refocus on your goal or vision, reach out your arm in front of you. As you reach out and touch your goal, think about the photo you took of you achieving your vision – pull back to the photo image that you stored safely in your mind. Picture yourself in the image and start to get back to feeling all the feelings that you felt when you achieved your goal.

Breathe in every little detail …

Savour the feelings.

Open your eyes and start to take in your surroundings, holding onto those feelings of joy, happiness, gratefulness and abundance. You feel fulfilled, as you carry on with your day.

Nature's garden

Positive affirmations encouraging the client
to remain in the moment

Diane Jennings

Now you're resting so comfortably, just floating and drifting, take a lovely deep breath in and out; listen to the sounds all around you, notice them and let them go. And just imagine now you are walking slowly down a country lane. Feel the cool, stone wall and the moss growing up through the cracks. You can hear the sounds of nature all around.

You stop for a moment. You can hear the birds singing, the beautiful nature all around. You notice in the distance *a shimmering light*. It draws you nearer, you feel it like a magnet pulling you closer and closer. The light is coming from the most magical well, almost like a wishing well.

You walk closer and closer. You feel safe and protected as you walk towards the wishing well. You can hear quiet, calming voices, almost fairy-like. It takes you a moment to tune in. You hear magical, kind words – you are amazing, you are strong, you are unique, you are special – you feel these words are just for you.

You decide to sit down next to this beautiful wishing well and close your eyes for a moment. And while you're resting there comfortably, you can feel an inner peace, a calm tranquillity filling you, helping you to notice all the positives in your life – helping you to drift away from all the challenges that life can bring.

You hear the voices gently guiding you, filling you with complete confidence, knowing that you can choose the right way for you. You rise up now, feeling completely at ease with the universe, at peace with yourself.

You start to walk slowly back to the country lane, back towards your final destination. But you now know you can choose which is the right way for you because you are your own expert, you know what is right for you.

And you realise now that the most important thing in life is to remain in the moment. It's important not to worry about what has happened in the past or, more importantly, what might happen in the future. Spending time in the moment and being at peace with yourself and others is the most important thing in life.

Room of confidence

Connect with confidence from within and recognise
you can have confidence whenever you need it

Clare Murchison

So, it's time to relax, knowing that the confident you, the capable you, the you that can do the things you want – calmly, confidently and radiating self-assurance – is always there ready to unleash, ready to call on, always within you.

Perhaps you'll gently close your eyes as you take three long, slow, deep breaths.

Breathe in slowly and deeply – breathing in through your nose and out through your mouth.

Breathing in calm positive energy.

Breathing out worries and anxieties.

Breathe in calm, breathe out stress.

Breathe calmly and deeply, releasing any tension in your mind and your body.

Each easy breath relaxing you further still.

Feeling a calmness deep within you with each breath that you take, knowing that …

When you are calm and relaxed the confident you shines through.

When you are calm and relaxed you connect more with the strengths and resources that are within you.

When you are calm and relaxed you feel more confident and the more confidence you radiate.

Now I want you to imagine a warm white light flowing around you, enveloping you, surrounding you, comforting you, protecting you.

And imagine that warm white light flowing through your whole body, releasing any tension and releasing the real you once again – calm, confident, positive and self-assured.

The warm white light flows down through the top of your head, relaxing all those little muscles and the skin of your scalp. Flowing through the muscles of your face … your forehead, your eyes and eyelids … your cheeks, mouth and jaw muscles …

The warm white light gradually spreads through your whole body, travelling down through your neck and shoulder muscles and into your back. And, as you relax more and more, the warm white light moves down through your arms and into your hands down to the very tips of your fingers and tips of your thumbs.

The warm white light releases any tension in the chest and stomach – spreading a kind of warm and comfortable sort of feeling that flows into every cell of your body and the spaces between each cell.

The warm light passes down through your thigh muscles, down through your shins and calves and all the way down to the very tips of your toes.

The warm white light envelops your whole body as every muscle relaxes and lets go.

Every muscle of your body is beautifully relaxed and easy and your mind is relaxed too, a kind of warm, comfortable sort of feeling that flows into every cell and fibre of your entire being.

Just let your mind and your imagination drift and … imagine you are standing at the top a beautiful staircase, simply following the sound of my voice as I count backwards from ten to zero and you find yourself relaxing more and more:

10 … take the first step down now, relaxing and letting go.

9 … relaxing more and more, no need to hurry.

8 … your breathing becoming slower and steadier.

7 … drifting deeper and deeper.

6 … deeper still, just let go.

5 … really relaxing now.

4 … becoming calmer and calmer.

3 … drifting deeper than ever before.

2 … more and more relaxed.

1 … all the way down to zero.

And you find yourself in a beautiful room. A room that is just perfect for you, filled with soft light and furniture, pictures and possessions that bring you happiness and joy. As you look around, you notice a comfortable chair. A luxurious, welcoming, comfy chair … and you wander across and settle back into the cushions, allowing your body to be supported and cocooned by that luxurious chair. And, as you relax more and more, your mind begins to drift.

It drifts back to a time when you were so confident, so in control, so self-assured.

And you picture that time, noticing how you are standing, how you hold your head, your shoulders, your body, moving easily with power and grace. You notice the tilt of your head, the energy that is flowing about you, how you smile.

You can see where your eyes are focused and what you are choosing to pay attention to.

You hear the tone and pace of your voice, instantly recognisable as that confident you, which you can be whenever you choose to be, whenever you wish, simply by trusting yourself and your abilities.

You are radiating confidence, that confidence that comes from deep within you. And you feel proud. Proud of how tall you are standing. How self-assured your every move is. How clearly you speak with such grace, such poise. Trusting yourself, trusting your abilities, trusting your judgement.

So, you savour that moment. Committing it firmly to memory. Enjoying that confident and self-assured you – the real you.

Now I want you to see yourself in the future, maybe next week, next year, in the next hour, in control, disregarding any troubles or what others may or may not think … and you are calm, relaxed, poised, competent and confident. Create a vivid picture in your mind.

What can you see?

Where are you?

What can you hear?

Who is with you?

How do you feel?

How do you know that you are confident, calm and in control?

Take a moment as I go quiet to feel that confidence flowing through you, that inner trust that you have in your abilities, your judgement. Just enjoy that confident you. Keep picturing this confident you. Focus on that feeling of confidence, of quiet self-assurance, of that calm, relaxed sensation that is within you.

Now that you have connected with that confidence, you realise more and more that confidence is always there. It never leaves you. It may be hidden for a while, but it's always there whenever you wish to connect to it. Whenever you want to, whenever you choose to.

You are realising, more and more, that confidence comes from believing that you are good enough and that you have the ability to do the things you want to do, those things you choose to do.

Trust you are capable, believe you are confident, and you are confident. You can access this feeling of confidence whenever you choose to simply by using the power of your mind.

Calm, relaxed and confident is simply a habit, a way of being, an attitude of mind. The more you practice being that calm, relaxed and confident you, the more you develop that ability. When you act calm, relaxed and confident then you are seen by others to be calm, relaxed and confident, and you feel calm, relaxed and confident, and you are calm, relaxed and confident.

You can see yourself now – relaxed, calm, confident, in control and fully aware of how good this feels, how easy it feels and knowing this is how you are the best version of you. Relaxed and confident in every situation, in every choice you make, in everything you say …

You will awake refreshed and happy, confident in your ability to create that feeling of confidence, knowing that you have all the strengths and resources you need to be that person you want to be – calm, confident and self-assured.

You now take a deep breath with the image of you in your mind of you – calm and relaxed, confident and self-assured, comfortable and radiating confidence as you tell yourself how confident you really are today, tomorrow and every day.

The right decision

A story metaphor to encourage self-confidence and trust in making our own choices in life

Paula Greensted

The young woman followed the estate agent from room to room, her heart sinking. The house was in a very desirable area – everyone said so – and the stylish décor was straight from the pages of a magazine. It had a sleek little kitchen, its polished surfaces gleaming, and a window that looked out over the modern minimalist garden. She could see the neighbouring properties above the fence, all equally pristine and well-kept. Everything was perfect. Yet she knew this was not the place for her.

'There's been a lot of interest already,' the agent remarked as they ended the tour. 'Houses in this location are highly sought after.'

The young woman nodded sadly, knowing this was true. She had spent months poring over property details and listening to advice, so she understood the elements of a good investment. Everybody had been keen to point out exactly what she needed. Somewhere in the right position and with kerb appeal, they said. She listened carefully to all their opinions, as she did in almost every area of life. Now having saved long and hard for a home of her own, she felt the weight of making a sensible choice.

Someone had recommended the smart new apartments being built in town. But the only outside space was a small balcony with nothing green in sight. 'Low maintenance, that's just what you want,' said the friend. 'Because a garden takes upkeep and experience.' *A garden takes patience and love*, thought the young woman, as she looked up at the soulless grey block.

Another friend pointed out an older but newly renovated property. 'All the hard work's been done for you,' they told her. 'You don't want to be tackling building projects without the proper know-how.' She could not admit that she rather liked the idea of learning new skills and being creative.

Nothing ticked all the right boxes. Friends and family found many faults: ugly windows, gardens that faced the wrong direction or too many cars parked in the street. Once she did find somewhere she rather liked but her colleagues at work had counselled strongly against it. It stood beside a children's playground, and they believed any noise might affect the property's future value. Privately, she considered the sounds of laughter and play to be priceless.

Then her brother, who was something of an expert, had proposed a viewing of the house in which she now stood. 'It's ideal,' he told her. 'In a very select neighbourhood. Just right for you.'

But it wasn't right and now the estate agent had nothing else to show her. The only other property on his books in her price range was a cottage outside town that did not match her advised tick list at all. The young woman pondered on this, remembering all the times she had allowed her life to be shaped by other people's opinions instead of her own. She wondered how it might feel to trust her own judgment for a change.

'I'd like to view the cottage,' she told the agent, surprising them both. 'As soon as possible.'

And so, she found herself driving out of town along a winding country lane, the hedgerows thick with wildflowers. She opened the window and let the breeze blow in, feeling her spirits lift for the first time in months. Following the agent's directions, she passed a farm and several houses until she came to a pair of cottages set back from the lane. The one on the left-hand side was pretty, its windows sparkling in the sun. Children's laughter could be heard from inside and a small tricycle lay abandoned on the lush green lawn.

The 'For Sale' board was outside the cottage on the right, a tired version of its twin, run down and in need of some attention. But, as the young woman stepped out of her car, she noticed the beautiful wisteria that flourished around the porch. She recalled with a smile how, as a child, she loved to watch her grandfather pruning the violet blooms that clustered around his garden wall. He taught her the names of the other plants he grew and how to look after them.

As she pushed open the rickety wooden gate, she saw some of those very same specimens growing in beds on either side of the front path, among a tangle of weeds. The garden wrapped around the cottage, and it wasn't hard to imagine how lovely it might look with a little care and time. She approached the faded front door and knocked – loudly, because the agent had told her the vendor was quite deaf. There followed the sound of shuffling steps and then an elderly lady appeared in the doorway, beaming brightly.

'You're here!' the lady said, almost as if she recognised the young woman, and beckoned her inside. 'You have a good look round by yourself, dear – the stairs are a bit much for me these days. I'll make us a cup of tea for when you're done.'

The young woman wandered through the cottage. She loved it instantly. It was far from large and needed updating but she knew without doubt that it was meant for her. Every room was welcoming, ready for her mark to be made upon it. This time she was certain.

From the landing window, she looked down at the rear garden and fields beyond, planning exactly how she wanted her home to be. She had no need to ask anyone else. Of course, she understood there might be mistakes along the way, but they would be hers and she would learn from them.

As she headed back downstairs, she caught sight of her reflection in a mirror on the wall. She looked different somehow, confident, her eyes lit with excitement.

She followed the sound of a whistling kettle towards her future.

CHAPTER SEVEN

Just relax

Breathing in the light

A soothing relaxation to calm body and mind using the breath

Sarah Bamber

Let's take a nice slightly deeper than normal breath, in and out, gently closing your eyes or lowering your gaze to reduce distractions.

When you are ready, we'll do this again, but this time let's release a little sigh as we breathe out, sigh inwardly to yourself or out loud (whichever you are most at ease with).

On our next breath in, we're going to gently raise our shoulders towards our ears – feeling a slight contraction in the neck and shoulder muscles.

Now, gently exhale and slowly lower the shoulders away; feel a gentle push as they lower, allowing any tightness in your neck, chest and shoulders to simply relax and melt away …

Okay, that's lovely.

With our next breath in, we're going to turn our attention to where we are … feel your seat bones on the chair beneath you, your feet on the floor or feel the mattress/duvet/blanket below you on the bed. Breathe in … feel your weight on the chair or bed beneath you … breathe out – feeling safe …

Breathing in through your nose, feeling the air entering your chest, feel as it fills your lungs, as the air fills your belly like a balloon. Exhale now through your mouth, completely emptying the air from your lungs …

With your next breath in, imagine the breath as a cleansing breath, cleansing and purifying as it fills your lungs, the air sweeping into your body … as you exhale, imagine any negative thoughts leaving your body with the breath …

Now, as you sit or lie there relaxing, imagine a white ray of light hovering above your head ... It is a beautiful and warming light.

With your next breath in, imagine the beautiful light moving with your breath ... imagine the warming ray of light passing over your head, over your skull, your forehead, over your nose, lips and chin ... entering your lungs, warm and calming ... and, as you release your breath, feel as it cleanses and washes away your anxiety, exhaling your worries and fears ...

Allow the light to linger around your head ... Now, as you breathe in, imagine the calming, beautiful white light flowing down your arms, your elbows, forearms, inside and out, down your wrists, hands and fingers, imagine it filling the cells in your body, filling them with peace and calm. Feel the tension and anxiety being washed away as you release the breath ... allowing the light to linger.

With your next breath in, the light travels down over your neck, your chest and ribs, the whole upper torso, both front and back, inside and out, all filled with beautiful, energising light. Release the breath, release the tiredness and tension held in your upper body ... allowing the light to linger.

Now, as you breathe in, let the light flow over your lower body, front and back, inside and out, feel the warm and peaceful light slowly move over your hips, your thighs ... warming your knees, shins ... your ankles, feet and toes ... cleansing and energising as it flows over you ... the light lingers a little longer.

And this time, as you release the breath ... imagine the light moving out of your body through the tips of your toes ... imagine all the negative energy coming out of your toes like strings of spaghetti ... the light leaving your body and falling to the ground ... being absorbed by the earth ... the tension going down, down into the ground ... all tension, negativity, worry and fear dissolving into the earth.

Breathe normally for a few breaths now, relaxed, feeling cleansed and refreshed ... breathing in and breathing out ... feeling peaceful.

Now, a much brighter light appears above your head ... it shines like a beautiful jewel ... imagine a dazzling diamond caught in the sunlight ... it hovers above you ...

And, as you relax here under the beautiful light, gently breathing in and out ... it starts to slowly move over your body, scanning from the top of your head, moving slowly down ... as it scans down over your body, you feel it filling you with its warmth, with calm, with peace and joy, all the way down towards the tips of your toes. Feel the warmth … the calm … the peace … the joy …

The light lingers again, completely covering you from head to toe … it waits … checking to make sure there are no signs of tension or worry left.

Once it is sure, it leaves you, dissolving into the ground, taking with it any last remnants of negative energy.

Stay here in this moment, breathing in and out, enjoying the warmth it leaves behind … notice how your body feels … notice how your mind feels.

Feel the peace and calm …

With our next breath in, we're going to slowly turn our attention to where we are … bringing our focus back into the room where we started our relaxation … feel the chair beneath you, your feet on the floor or feel the bed beneath your body. Breathe in … start to wiggle your fingers and toes … slowly bringing your mind and body back into the room as you breathe out.

When you are ready, slowly open your eyes, blinking and giving them time to focus.

Take a few moments to reflect, still feeling the peace and calm within you. Stay here as long as you like … knowing this peace and calm is always within reach.

In your own time, slowly rise up and enjoy the rest of your day.

Colour of love

Release tense muscles and relax deeply using the
healing power of colour

Clare Murchison

Settle back now, making yourself comfortable. Perhaps stretching out as you
allow your arms and legs, your feet and hands to relax, to settle with no
effort at all.

And, as you relax, more and more, you feel that sensation of letting go
flowing down through your whole body as any tension simply drains away.
Every muscle, every cell and the space between each cell relaxed.

Your thoughts quieten as you listen to the sound of my voice, knowing
that you have nowhere else to be right now and nothing else to do except relax.
Drifting deeper and deeper with each word I speak and each breath you take.
Your eyes close as you relax more and more with the rhythm of your breath,
as you drift deeper and deeper, guided by the sound of my voice.

I want you to imagine a colour. Perhaps your favourite colour or the first
colour that comes to mind. And if you choose to change the colour as you
relax, more and more, then that's fine too. Just sense that colour, perhaps
altering the tone or the brightness or the shade until it feels like the perfect
colour for you.

As you relax, more and more, I want you to imagine that colour flowing
through your body, releasing any tension. As the colour flows down through
the top of your head, relaxing all those little muscles in your scalp and face,
relaxing your forehead and your eyes and eyelids, your cheeks and jaw
muscles.

The colour flows through your neck and shoulders into the top of your arms, letting any tension drain away as it flows down through your elbows, into your forearms, through your wrists and into your hands, right the way down to the very tips of your fingers.

And, as you relax more and more, allowing the colour to gradually spread, so that it begins to envelop your whole body. A warm and comfortable sort of feeling that floods into every fibre of your entire being, releasing any tension – every muscle relaxed, every cell relaxed – as the colour flows through your spine and across your back … just letting those muscles relax and let go as the colour passes down through your thighs into your shins and calves. The colour radiates into your feet, down to the very tips of your toes. All the muscles of your body are beautifully relaxed and easy, very lazy and your mind is relaxed too.

Let your mind and your imagination drift, feeling lazy, easy, relaxed and comfortable. I want you to imagine that you can see yourself standing at the top of ten steps. You are standing at the top of ten steps now, looking down, and as I count down from ten to zero, you are going to see yourself and feel yourself walking down each step, relaxing more and more:

10 … take the first step down now, relaxing and letting go.

9 … every muscle, every cell in your body is relaxed.

8 … drifting down easily now.

7 … drifting deeper and deeper.

6 … as every sound takes you deeper still.

5 … drifting deeper than you ever have before.

4 … your breathing becoming calmer and calmer.

3 … calmer still now.

2 … feeling more and more relaxed.

1 … just sleep deeply.

And now, feeling deeply and beautifully relaxed, you drift into a deep and relaxing sleep, and …

Desert island

To focus the client on the present moment

Diane Jennings

While you are relaxing there so comfortably … so peacefully … I want you to imagine you are stepping onto a beautiful magic carpet … it feels warm, soft and safe beneath your feet. You settle yourself onto the majestic rug and close your eyes. You take a moment to breathe in the warm, clear air, and breathe out any cares of the day … Notice the rise and fall of your chest.

The carpet rises with you safely on board … it floats higher and higher into the clear blue sky … you can hear nothing but the wind flowing past you. As you rise up and up … you can feel all your worries and cares being left behind … Helping you to feel lighter and lighter.

The beautiful carpet is taking you on a magical journey … an escape from the rest of the world … there is really nothing for you to do … the carpet knows exactly where you want to go … It finds a wonderful landing place on your own special beach … The sand is white, super fine and soft, there are palm trees everywhere … the warm sun is gently hitting your skin … the breeze is blowing gently through your hair … you can hear the sound of waterfalls … this place is your own special place … a place where you can find your own peace and tranquillity … It's a perfect desert island especially for you.

You start to walk up the beach on this paradise island and notice all the natural beauty … you feel at peace with the world around you … You follow the sound of a waterfall … guided only by the sound of the trickling, flowing water.

You find this amazing scene … with the warm sun catching the mist of the water droplets … creating a magical rainbow … you notice the end of the rainbow melts into a pool of cool, clear water … and it's here you find peace with the world … it's here at the pool of all knowledge … that you realise the most important thing in life is the present moment … the here and now … not focusing on the past or the future but enjoying the moment … this very moment … because we know the things we worry about may not happen anyway … anxiety is just our thought patterns accumulating and trapping us in that cycle of negative thinking … Why not focus on what you can do, rather than what you can't do … as this will move you to the positive aspects of living … helping you to notice the positives in your life.

You sit and ponder these thoughts for a while and, while you're sitting there, I want to tell you a story … (now use a metaphor story to affirm the present)

Meditative breathing technique

Switch off the mind with this short, focused breath work meditation

Emma Last

Close your eyes and start by focusing on your breathing. Put your hands on your diaphragm and start to feel the breath coming into your body, making sure that you can feel the rise and fall of your hands.

By focusing on your breathing, you are allowing your mind to calm and relax. Feel the weight of your body move closer to the ground as you relax.

Breathe in … and breathe out …

Breathe in … and breathe out …

Breathe in … and breathe out …

Feel the parts of your body that are starting to relax and feel those stresses float away.

Continue to feel your breath enter and leave your body.

Now deepen your relaxation by using what we call square breathing:

Breathe in for 4 … 1, 2, 3, 4

Hold for 4 … 1, 2, 3, 4

Breathe out for 4 … 1, 2, 3, 4

Hold for 4 … 1, 2, 3, 4

Make sure that the breaths that you are breathing out are as focused and important as the breaths that you are breathing in.

Again:

Breathe in for 4 … 1, 2, 3, 4

Hold for 4 … 1, 2, 3, 4

Breathe out for 4 … 1, 2, 3, 4

Hold for 4 … 1, 2, 3, 4

Continue to slowly feel your breaths enter and leave your body. Let your breathing slow with your body as you deepen your relaxation. Keep doing this until you feel you are relaxed.

Simple progressive muscle relaxation

Relax your mind as you relax your body

Emma Last

Breathing normally, lying on your back or sitting comfortably, mentally tense the top of your head and relax it, making sure you are focusing on feeling the difference in the tense and relaxed states in your body.

Tense and relax your forehead, tense and relax … your eyes, your nose, your cheeks, your mouth, and your jaw.

Now start to work on tensing and relaxing down your body, from your neck, shoulders, the tops of your arms to the bottom, to your wrists and onto your hands; clench your hands tightly and relax them, slowly uncurling and feeling the relaxation in your fingers and fingertips.

Tense and relax your stomach, lower back, hips, thighs, knees, calves, ankles, feet and finally your toes.

CHAPTER EIGHT

Letting go

A meadow walk

Letting go of the past

Diane Jennings

And now you're so wonderfully relaxed, I want you just to imagine you're strolling down a country lane, the warm sun on your face, the breeze blowing through your hair. You take a nice, long deep breath in and out; notice how you feel. You look up and see the leaves on the trees, beautiful colours, greens, yellows, oranges and reds, all those vibrant colours.

As you stroll lazily along this road, you notice a glimmer of water in the distance, the shimmer of the light drawing you nearer and nearer. As you approach this wonderful stream, you hear the gurgle of the water as it flows past you, notice a small fish swim on by, smell the fresh crispness of the air. It's a fascinating place. As you look around, you notice a small, smooth rock. You gently sit down on the warm surface, and you take a long, slow deep breath in.

And, as you gaze at the flowing water, you realise you can't control what is happening around you. You can only control how you react to the situation. So, now take a deep breath in as you choose to let go of all the negative energy, noticing the ground beneath you. Give yourself permission to feel, to be and to let go. Choose to find that peace and tranquillity that you know is vital to your well-being.

Breathe in, breathe out. As you begin to take in those lovely deep breaths, I want you to see a beautiful, radiant light all around you – it may be white or any other colour that you feel drawn to – and just imagine this amazing colour filling you with a calm, peaceful tranquillity; welcome this colour.

Notice this radiant light as it flows through you, allowing it to heal you, helping you to feel more able to cope. Inhale that amazing calmness and exhale any dark grey energy that's held within. Letting go of all those worries and cares, feeling only positive thoughts and hope for the future. Create that beautiful intention of letting go of all that doesn't serve you. With every exhalation, let all the weight drop from your shoulders.

And now, as we continue to go deeper, notice your thoughts and feelings. You are in control of your own peace, your own happiness and your own well-being. You rise up from the beautiful smooth rock and start to wander further along the stream, turning your head to the warm sun. You notice a beautiful, bright colourful meadow, masses of amazing, colourful flowers. You take a moment to notice the here and now. Isn't it pleasant to be in the moment, not worrying about the future or the past, but enjoying the moment? As we both know, the things we worry about may not happen anyway, the things we worry about won't happen anyway, as worries drop out of our life.

And while you're standing there amongst the beautiful flowers, I want to tell you a story …

Beach stroll

Relaxation and release tension

Diane Jennings

While you're resting so comfortably, taking the image into your mind of you, filled with a warm air, slowly breathing out, releasing any tension in your body as you slowly exhale.

Now just allow your breathing to fall into a natural rhythm. Imagine you're walking alongside a sandy shore, feel the warm sand on your feet, the sun on your back and your shoulders.

Hear the sound of the waves, notice the blues and greens of the ever-changing flow. You look up at the clear blue sky. Notice the seagulls as they fly and play in the cool breeze, calling out to each other. Observe the sea for a time, its steady, perpetual movement against the shore. Smell the scent of the salty air.

With each wave, you feel the calmness overtake you; as the wave drifts out, it takes with it all your worries and cares. Your whole body is relaxed now as you lay back on the soft, sandy shore and allow pleasant thoughts to float and drift.

As you lie there, just floating and drifting, you feel complete peace and tranquillity, it is time out of time. Your body and mind floating with the winds of change. The ebb and flow of the ocean, bringing healing and serenity to you. Enjoy being in this quiet place, this haven of peace …

Effortless ocean

A deeply relaxing guided hypnosis script
to bring inner peace and balance

Caroline Measures

Take a long, deep breath in and just hold it there for a few seconds … and, as you exhale, allow your eyes to close and see if you can let go of any tension held in your body just now … That's right … Release anything you've been holding on to, either consciously or unconsciously. Release it now … Good … With every breath you take, you can feel more and more relaxed, more and more peaceful … Just letting go … Choosing to release anything that no longer serves you, any stress, any discomfort, letting it all go now … Allowing it to flow out of your body, out of your mind … flowing down your arms into your hands and fingertips and out of your body … flowing down your legs into your feet and toes and out of your body, melting away from your face, your neck, your shoulders, out of your head … release …

You're about to go on a journey into deep, deep relaxation. My voice will go with you, and you will be guided into a soft, comfortable resting space, just like the moment right before you fall asleep at night or the moment just as you are waking up in the morning … A moment of suspended awareness where you can float on a soft, warm blanket of relaxation, like cotton-wool clouds and feather-down pillows. A whisper among the trees, calling you further and further into the sanctuary of peaceful slumber …

Sinking, sinking, sinking … into the most comfortable mattress you've ever lain on … where you can rest your body and surrender to the soft warmth … feeling held … supported … and relaxed … in this safe, comfortable place … feeling heavier and heavier … deeper and deeper … more and more relaxed …

In your mind, I'd like you to imagine you are standing at the top of some steps leading down onto a beautiful sandy beach. Make your way down the steps, one at a time, 10 … 9 … 8 … 7 … 6 … 5 … 4 … 3 … 2 … 1 … stepping down onto the warm, soft sand. Feel it between your toes as you start to walk along. The sun is warm on your skin … the breeze is gentle … waves are lapping on the shore …

You have all the time in the world, as you stroll along the beach, picking up the occasional jewel-like shell … all the time in the world … so slow … so graceful …

As you walk along, you notice a thin wall of mist hanging in the air across the sand in front of you … it shimmers with rainbows and swirling vapour … you can approach it and carry on walking right through, stepping into bright sunshine once again on the other side. Make your way to the shoreline, where the aquamarine waves wash the sand over and over and over again … Pick up a stick or use your finger or foot and write your name in the fine grains … watch as the next wave erases the letters … write the word "calm" … and watch as the letters are washed away … now write "peace" … and see the word washed away … write "relax" … and again the water clears it all away … write "worries" and have them washed away … write "fears" and see them disappear … "stress" erased by the waves … write whatever comes to mind and just observe how effortlessly the sea dissolves the words, the problems, the feelings, all back to neutral … everything in perfect balance … only the present moment existing …

Further along the shore, there is a large hammock hanging up between two palm trees. This is here just for you to rest in for a while. It's easy to sit down into and recline, so that your head is nestled on the pillow and the rest of your body is fully supported and comfortable in the soft fold of the fabric. The trees provide enough shade from the sun, and you can just gaze out to sea to the horizon where the sea meets the sky. Your eyelids start to feel heavy, so heavy that you can hardly keep them open. It's easier to let them close and surrender to complete relaxation. Listen to the sound of the waves as they swoosh over the sand, coming and going, all by themselves, just like the breath, in and out … in and out … in and out … Listen to the birds circling overhead, calling to each other high up above … feeling the golden sun's rays warming your skin through the shady leaves of the palm trees …

as, the hammock rocks gently from side to side in time to its own lullaby, as you fall deeper and deeper asleep … in and out … in and out … relax … so peaceful … in and out … relax here for a while …

(Pause for a few minutes.)

Shadows are lengthening across the shore and the sun begins to dip lower in the sky, sending streaks of gold, pink, orange and red across the sea. It's time for you to return gently to the here and now. Feeling deliciously relaxed and at ease, you can climb out of the hammock and take a good look at the natural beauty all around you. When you're ready, make your way back along the shore towards the veil of mist. Effortlessly pass through and step out into the sunshine on the other side. The air is warm, the breeze so soothing against your skin. Walk to the steps that brought you here and go up them one at a time, getting ready to wake up feeling refreshed and at peace, stepping up, 1 … 2 … 3 … starting to feel more alert, 4 … 5 … feeling more awake now, 6 … 7 … feeling more alert and ready to wake up, 8 … 9 … and 10 … opening your eyes and feeling fully refreshed and composed, as the tranquillity of the beach carries on into the next moments of your day.

Meeting a new version of you

A calming relaxation promoting confidence and positive change

Kathleen Bradley

First of all, just allow your eyes to close. What can you see behind your closed eyes? Colours, shapes or maybe it's just a dark colour? And that's okay.

All I ask from you now is to just concentrate on my voice, the soothing, comforting sound of my voice.

And at this time, nobody needs or wants anything from you because this time is for only you, no one else; this is your time, time to allow yourself to relax and enjoy this wonderful, healing, hypnotic trance.

And every time you hear the word RELAX, you go even more relaxed, even more comfortable, and every time you hear the word DEEPER, you will go more deeply relaxed. So down you go, even deeper now.

This is your special time, just for you.

And I'd like you to use your wonderful imagination and imagine seeing a beautiful big ball of golden light hovering just above your head; you can feel it, so warm so comforting.

And now this big beautiful ball of golden light is coming down and covering your forehead and every nerve … every muscle in your forehead is relaxing now, let your eyelids relax, it's now covering your nose, cheekbones and the back of your head and, as it comes down to your mouth and jaw, you can feel your tongue resting at the bottom of your mouth, your whole head and face now enveloped in this beautiful golden, healthy, healing light.

So now I want you to RELAX even more, even DEEPER, down you go. This beautiful ball of golden light is going down your neck, into your shoulders, straight down your arms, into your elbows, your wrists and straight to the tips of your fingers. Take notice of how your fingers feel, perhaps they're tingly or even heavy.

Even more comforting now, relaxing even more, RELAX even deeper down.

Now, this beautiful golden light is coming into your chest, every nerve, every muscle, every cell, relaxing even more. Down into your tummy, into your waist and straight down your entire back, through to your buttocks, so relaxed, so comfortable, feeling so at ease, so safe now.

And now this beautiful golden light is coming down your legs, into your thighs, your knees, your calves, your shins and ankles, and straight down to the tips of your toes. You can feel your whole body enveloped in this beautiful golden light, it feels so comfortable, so good for you to have your special time just for you, time you deserve to enjoy this wonderful hypnotic trance.

And now, you're so relaxed, I want you to go even deeper, ten times deeper, ten times more relaxed, down you go.

And now you're so relaxed, I want to talk to a part of you that's always listening, the part that is responsible for you from the minute you took your first breath, your subconscious mind.

This part is responsible for all your learned behaviour, like walking, talking, all your skills, like driving, riding a bike, all your learned skills. Can you imagine if every day you had to remember how to walk? Which foot first, get your balance, how difficult would this be? We take all this for granted and only realise how much we need these skills if we were have an accident and struggle to walk. When we were little, we perhaps learned a nursery rhyme, and we still remember every word, even now, after all these years, how good is our subconscious mind for remembering so much, all our learned behaviours?

Our subconscious mind doesn't know the difference between fake or real. If we practise things daily, it becomes our learned behaviour. So, I'm going to ask the part of your subconscious mind now to come forward and remove all the unwanted thoughts, feelings and behaviours that you no longer need, that are no use to you any more. So can you do this now please, release and let go of the things that you don't want or need any more, unhealthy feelings, or thoughts that are making life hard, difficult or unhealthy for you.

Just like having a good clear out of your wardrobe, stuff that's very old, tatty or just doesn't fit any more, how good does that feel?

So, I will go quiet for a few minutes while you chuck all of those things away for good.

(Pause for a few minutes.)

So still, so relaxed now, even more than before, RELAX.

We have some room for new behaviours, perhaps a new hobby, or a new career, or to be healthier. You can think of some new exciting goals you would like to achieve and start this new learned behaviour, which will fit in your wardrobe so easily now.

How good will that feel? Picture yourself now, see yourself having achieved this and see yourself smiling and feeling so proud, and all your loved ones looking at you, smiling also. And this feeling will grow every day, just like a snowball, getting bigger and brighter every day.

And now I'm going to gently wake you. I'm going to count down from five to one, and when I reach one, you will open your eyes and feel so good, so much better than before, having enjoyed this lovely, peaceful, relaxing time, so here we go: Five, waking slowly, four, gently waking now, three, feelings coming back now in your fingers and toes, two and one, wake now.

Night flight

Letting go of that which does not serve you and opening
your mind to new perspectives and insights

Clare Murchison

As you drift deeper and deeper, you drift into an easy and comforting sleep. And as you sleep, you have a dream. You dream that it is a balmy, warm night as you gaze up at the vast midnight-blue expanse above you. A canopy of dark velvet studded with the pinpricks of starlight like diamonds in the sky. The flickering lights of satellites travelling high above in the night sky are obscured at times by almost ghost-like floating clouds. Moonbeams scatter across the earth, illuminating the foliage and creating an ethereal beauty all around you. There is a stillness and a sense of wonder and possibility in the air.

The call of an owl stirs your senses as you watch it glide overhead in the moon-kissed sky. Hunting, searching, waiting, gliding in the soft currents of air, at one with nature. And then you realise that the owl is waiting for you. Waiting for you to fly with it in the heavenly night sky, high above the earth. And you know, even though you don't know how you know, that you can fly in the serenity of the dark night sky. You have always been able to fly.

The sensation of power and weightlessness is exhilarating as you lift your feet from the earth, arms outstretched, embracing the opportunity, trusting yourself to do this. And you feel free. Blissfully free. At one with the world. At one with nature. At one with yourself. Instinctively flying, trusting your inner self as you soar upwards beside the owl. The wind carrying you high above the landscape, supporting you, transporting you, is cool and refreshing.

Gliding effortlessly under the stars, you find yourself letting go of your fears and inhibitions, sensing that they are no longer any use to you. Letting go of anything that has been weighing you down. Let go of those disappointments, those people, those events and beliefs that hindered you, held you back, stopped you being who you were always meant to be. You cast them off into the atmosphere and find yourself soaring with more ease and grace as you simply let go of anything you no longer need. Just let it go. Let it drift away. You no longer need those thoughts, those beliefs. They no longer serve you.

And you feel so free, drifting on those currents of warm air, feeling lighter, unhindered and so sure of yourself, once again. Trusting in yourself and your abilities. Having faith in your choices and losing the need for approval as your courage soars too.

Companionably and silently gliding into the sparkling heavens alongside the owl, you find that the world looks so different from this vantage point. Your life seems so different as you reflect and float. You understand more and more that the world is the same and yet forever changing. Nothing lasts forever. Everything is in motion, nothing is static. You are becoming more aware that change is an absolute, just as day follows night and nothing stays the same. You are not the same, you are changing and you are so glad.

You are ready now. Ready to be the real you, once again. Ready to trust that you are enough. Ready to lose the masks, lose your inhibitions, your need to compare yourself unfavourably to others. Inspired by moonlight as you travel above this beautiful planet with a new perspective, you feel that connection with the you that you truly are strengthening. Up here you sense that your time is now. You are a person who can do anything you choose to do. You are able to trust your intuition, be guided by your inner voice to do what feels right. No longer will you put the needs of others first. You now know with certainty that you are utterly unique, a one off, a limited edition. You are here for a reason. You can do what you do in a way that no one else can do.

The vastness of the star-studded sky creates a feeling of timelessness where your past, your present and your future vie for attention in your mind and anything seems possible. You feel you could reach out and capture some tiny glittering stars to bring those sparkles back to your everyday life. And then you realise that there is no need as you have so many sparkling moments in your life already. So many good things that you hadn't really considered before or thought of in that way before come into your thoughts and you feel glad. Glad to be you. Glad to have the real you back again.

And you sense that the owl knows your night flight has achieved all that you needed as it swoops lower and lower toward the earth, and you follow, feeling that you have gained insights and a new perspective up in the night canopy.

Softly and gently, you drift back to the earth, feeling the solidity of the soil beneath your feet once again as the outline of the owl in the moonlight flies away, leaving you feeling at peace, wiser, lighter and ready to be the best possible version of you once again – the real you – and it feels really good.

Rest and recharge

A progressive relaxation script inviting you to connect
with the wisdom of your body

Pamela Gilvear

I would now like you to take your attention to your breath, start by taking a nice deep breath in, right down into your belly, feel your belly fill up and expand, hold your breath for a few seconds and then take a slow, gentle out breath.

And again, nice deep breath in, right down to your belly, feel your belly fill up and expand, hold your breath for a few seconds and then a slow, gentle out breath.

Do that once more, nice deep breath in, right down to your belly, feel your belly fill up and expand, hold your breath for a few seconds and then use a slow gentle out breath.

Now let your breath go back to its natural rhythm …

…

If at any time throughout this practice you notice discomfort, tension or feelings of restriction in the body, breathe into this area.

As you breathe in, have a sense of your breath dissolving, dispersing whatever discomfort is there for you, letting it go on the out breath. You may wish to visualise it floating away on a cloud …

…

Let's create some space now to fully connect with your beautiful body that holds so much wisdom.

I would like you to start by taking your attention to your feet, both of your feet, observe without judgement, how they feel right in this moment ...

...

What sensations are there? ...

...

Notice the temperature of your feet ...

...

Notice your toes, balls of your feet, arches, heels, top of your feet, noticing without judgement how they feel.

If judgment comes up, just allow it to pass, letting it go, let it be carried away on your next out breath, never to return.

If at any point your mind wanders, just bring your attention back to wherever we are in this practice ...

...

Now I would like you to move your attention to your legs, slowly moving up your legs, through your ankles, shins, calves, knees, to your thighs ...

...

Just notice how they feel.

What sensations are present? ...

...

Notice the temperature of your legs ...

...

You may notice different sensations and temperatures in different parts of your legs.

Notice without judgement what is there for you right in this moment.

If any tension, tightness, restrictions or discomfort is present, imagine it dissolving, dispersing on the in breath, leaving your body on the out breath, never to return ...

...

Now move your attention to your bottom, noticing where it makes contact with where you are, just observing how this feels in this moment, no judgment required, breathing in, dissolving and dispersing any tension, letting it go on the out breath ...

...

Take your focus now to your back, the whole of your back, lower, middle and your upper back. Observe how your back is feeling in this present moment ...

...

Notice any tension or discomfort, breathing into any areas of tension or discomfort, allowing it to dissolve and disperse, letting it go on the out breath.

Our backs are amazing, they support us throughout the day; you may wish to thank your back for its support.

Notice what your back needs in this moment ...

...

Move your attention now from your back to the back of your neck and up to your head.

Take time here to observe how these areas are feeling.

Is there any tension, discomfort, sensations present in the neck and head?

Breathe in to those places of discomfort, dissolving and dispersing, letting go on your out breath.

Remember, no judgment is required, we are purely observing what is here for you at this time.

Noticing if your attention wanders, gently bring it back to where we are in the practice ...

...

Now move your attention to your face, the whole of your face, your forehead, eyes, nose, cheekbones, lips, mouth, teeth, tongue, jaw.

Notice without judgment any tension that is present here ...

...

Gently allow the micro muscles around the eyes to soften and relax ...

...

Unclench your jaw and allow your tongue to rest gently in your mouth.

You may wish to bring a slight smile to your face, this lifts your energy, bringing feelings of warmth throughout your face and body.

This simple smile reduces stress and triggers the release of the feel-good neurotransmitters of dopamine, endorphins and serotonin.

Just allow this smile to spread through your entire being, sending waves of relaxation through your body ...

...

Shifting your attention now to your throat, just observing without judgment how this area feels.

Sometimes when we hold on to our words, we can have the sensation of needing to swallow in this area. Just notice what is here for you.

Breathe into any sensations which are present, dissolving, dispersing, letting go on the out breath …

…

Take your attention now to your shoulders, your arms; upper arms, elbows, lower arms, wrists, hands, fingers and thumbs. Just observe how they feel …

…

Shoulders can be an area where we hold a tremendous amount of tension. It may feel helpful to shrug your shoulders up towards your ears, then allowing them to drop. Do this a couple of times to help release the tension if needed …

…

Notice without judgment how the rest of your arms, hands, fingers and thumbs feel.

If at any point your mind wanders, just bring it back to where we are at in the practice …

…

Now move your attention to your chest area, your heart chakra, observing how this area feels, breathing into any tension/discomfort, with a sense of dissolving, dispersing and letting go on each out breath.

Enquire how your heart area is feeling.

Notice whatever sensations, words, maybe even memories come up for you in this area of the body.

We can build protection around our heart area to keep us safe from emotional pain. So, you may feel barriers, blocks, restrictions in this part of the body. This restricts the amount of love we can give and receive. Start to remove these barriers by noticing what is there for you. You may wish to visualise blocks being removed, or use your breath to shift them, with a sense of the blocks that no longer serve you being let go on your out breath …

…

Moving now to your stomach and your lower abdomen, observe what is here, noticing any tension, discomfort, restrictions, feelings of holding on to, feeling it dissolve and disperse on your out breath, a letting go, releasing …

…

Bring your attention now back down to your feet, resting here for a moment, then bring your whole body into your awareness, feel your whole body in this moment …

…

Now observe your whole body, the sensations and aliveness that are present …

…

Notice in this moment how your mind, body and soul are feeling.

You may find it helpful to give it a number, a percentage as an indication to you how much rest and recharge you need.

Just notice, without judgment, the number that floats in for you in this moment. This will give you an awareness of your body's energy levels, your internal 'battery level'.

It may be you're feeling exhausted right in this moment, with your energy levels very depleted, so you may feel your energy levels are low, around 10%.

You may feel tired, in need of some quiet time, time to rest your body in whatever way is helpful to you, you may notice the figure that pops in is around 50%.

Or you may be feeling energetically really good with the number that pops in around 80-100%.

Don't worry if you don't get a number, the most important aspect of this practice is to notice how your body is feeling, really tune in and hear what your body is communicating to you. Let it inform you in whatever way is best for you.

The healing ocean

Allow the ocean to help you let go of past trauma and welcome healing into your life

Maggie Matthews

Close your eyes ... take three deep breaths, breathing in through the nose and releasing through the mouth ... to help you let go of all the tensions of the day and release anything that you haven't dealt with, and just leave them all behind for now ... this is your time, this is your space for you to relax, to feel calm and to enjoy this time, which is especially for you. I would like you to take another deep breath and let it out slowly ... start to feel your body relax from the top of your head all the way down through to your shoulders ... down through your body, to the tip of your toes. Just let yourself feel calm, relaxed, peaceful and tranquil.

I would like you now to see yourself walking along a beautiful, golden, sandy beach with the sun shining brightly ... feeling the sun against your skin, warming your body ... feeling all of your muscles relaxing ... feeling the golden, soft sand between your toes underneath your feet.

You look up to see the clear blue sky, so vibrant and rich in colour ... you feel a sense of freedom and you sit down on the sand and soak up the sun. Listen to the waves of the sea crashing up against the rocks. Smell the sea air. Hear the shingle moving with the waves.

You can see the sun reflecting on the sea, like diamonds sparkling in the water. The waves are calling you, whispering your name, as they come up to the shore ... *I have been waiting for you to come to clear, cleanse and release anything from the past and present that no longer serves you. To bring you to a place of healing, love, peace, and clarity* … As you walk towards the water, you feel as if the sea is a magnet pulling you, inviting you, welcoming you into the healing warm water with open arms. The waves gently wash over your body as you walk deeper and deeper into the water. Let the water come up over your shoulders and around your face, as your body is lifting and getting lighter with the waves. You are floating on your back with the waves gently caressing you … your body feels light as a feather as all the negative emotions and feelings from the past and the present are being released into the water and washed away with the waves. The calming, relaxing, healing water is flowing through your cells and pores, cleansing and clearing you from anything that is holding you back from the past, which is blocking you from the present. Feel all of your senses coming alive and becoming renewed … with a new sense of freedom, confidence, positivity, love and happiness for yourself. Realise that it was only you holding yourself back and old beliefs from the past stopping you from moving forward … let go of people, places and situations that no longer serve you for your highest good. Let go, release and feel yourself reclaim your power and your self-worth … feel peace within you, a place of love, happiness and contentment … enjoy your newfound freedom on a mental, physical and emotional level.

As you float back to the shore, feeling a sense of tranquility, renewed energy and strength, you feel powerful and alive, as if you have been reborn.

The waves gently wash you back onto the beach, where you just sit and give gratitude to the sea for calling you, cleansing and clearing you.

The warmth of the sun on your back recharges and revitalises you … making you feel safe … giving you the clarity and inspiration that you need to move forward and embrace whatever life and each new day brings.

As you walk back across the beach, you are feeling lighter, more energised, with a new sense of self-worth, positivity and happiness. The love shines from within you and around you.

Accept yourself, love yourself and begin to come back slowly in a calm, peaceful and relaxed way.

The master painter

For the perfectionist who is already good enough

Clare Murchison

The man stood back, gazing at the canvas he was working on, the brush in his paint-stained fingers momentarily stilled in creation, appraising how each stroke was building a reality in oil that was unparalleled. A testament to his judgement, skill and intuitive trust in his ability to create the texture, the light, the colours that would bring dimensions of life on to a piece of fabric.

Perfection was rarely possible and never required. He could do things that others could not yet do, capturing what his patrons wanted whilst giving them more than they could ever imagine or perhaps comprehend.

Yet they rarely gave him time – the gift of time to create something so exquisite that it could never be bettered.

Didn't they realise that each picture was a process and to achieve perfection could take weeks, months, years?

Didn't they realise he required all the time he needed to create excellence?

He resented the eager requests as to the readiness of each portrait as he sought to improve the composition, editing strokes, layering the paint, adding more depth and differing pigments until he was almost satisfied. He couldn't understand the need to rush. He sensed he was creating more than a painting, even though that feeling was not something he could articulate.

Absorbed in his work, he didn't pause to acknowledge that his work was more than good enough and would be admired through the centuries.

Constantly striving to better the picture and not realising perhaps that the exquisitely painted hand was all that was needed to lift the painting to another level. He didn't consciously understand that the rest of the picture was simply a backdrop to the realistic depiction of the fold of the silk or how the enigmatic gaze of the sitter would capture the imagination of hundreds of thousands of humans across the centuries.

He felt time was constantly ebbing away. Each tick of the clock a signal that another moment had passed, never to be recaptured, just like the fleeting opportunity to sense something in the sitter of the portrait and immortalising that in oils and pigments. Capturing a moment in time for posterity not simply to hang on the walls of a grand house of a wealthy man.

As he created these canvases stroke by stroke, he was happily absorbed, doing what he loved, honing his skills still further, playing with colour, texture and light. Experimenting, toying with techniques, the light, the sitter. Focused yet open to possibilities, he trusted his instincts. Calm, relaxed and happy, he would tune into his higher self, painting in a way that seemed like his every brush stroke was inspired by a divine being. His focus was disturbed when he became frustrated with the demands of the patron; genius restored when he tuned in to the inner world of his subject and was intuitively guided how to translate hopes and dreams to canvas with ease. Just paint, just brush strokes. Transcending what should be possible to create photographic images with a depth of human understanding conveyed powerfully. Playing to his strengths. Listening to his heart. Guided by his inner voice.

And he remembered.

He remembered being the pupil.

The pupil that watched. Watching each stroke, each pause, each flicker of the eye. Noticing what happened on the canvas, at the paint table, the interaction between painter and subject. Tuning into the rhythm, the process and learning how he made his choices. He was the pupil privy to some of the artist's innermost thoughts and consideration.

And the pupil waited. Waiting for the day he would be recognised as a great artist too with wealthy merchants rewarding him handsomely. Waiting for the day he would step forward into his full potential. Knowing that he was more than good enough, he had always been good enough.

And the pupil painted. Painting in the quiet hours after the ingredients were prepared for the next day, the brushes cleaned and his master slept. He copied, he experimented, he tuned into his inner guide and, as he relaxed, he learnt to trust his judgement, his intuition, skills and capabilities.

Watching your worries float away

Connect with the wonders of nature as you let go of worry

Sarah Bamber

I'd like you to take a couple of nice gentle breaths in and out … and, when you are ready, slowly close your eyes or lower your gaze if you prefer.

Now, let's take a slightly deeper breath in – pausing briefly before releasing a long, slow breath out …

Let's repeat this breath again …

With your next inhale, imagine the sun shining down upon you and, as it does, a lovely warm wave of energy enters your body … with each exhale, watch as the wave of energy leaves your body, leaving you feeling calm and relaxed …

Carry on breathing in and out in this way for a few more breaths, noticing each breath as you feel your whole body becoming totally filled with this new energy.

Now, imagine you are going on a little journey …

It is a lovely warm, sunny day … a perfect day for a bike ride …

The sky is brilliant blue, not a cloud in sight … there's a gentle breeze blowing through your hair, and you can feel the cool breeze soothing your face …

The road ahead is clear, you are humming along to your favourite song, the scenery is filled with all the brightness of a summer's day …

Just ahead, at the side of the road, you notice a path between two tall trees. You are curious as to where this path leads … so you slow down, and slip off the seat, peering through the branches to get a better view …

You can see that the path leads away from the road, cutting its way down through the grass.

So, you leave the bike and start to follow the path through the tree branches into the tall grass ... the grass is swaying gently in the summer breeze ... you can feel it gently caressing your lower legs as you move through it along the path ...

The path starts heading slightly downhill and, after a short while, you notice a stream ahead of you. You continue to walk towards it ... then you notice a row of stepping stones going from one side of the stream to the other ... As you take off your shoes, the bank feels soft and damp ...

You can feel the warmth of the sun, so you raise your face upwards, absorbing its golden rays ... then you step forward into the cool water ... it feels so fresh and invigorating on your skin ...

You carefully step onto the first stone, the top peeping out of the water ... it feels so warm on your feet. You carry on carefully stepping from stone to stone until you reach a bigger stone in the middle of the stream. You carefully sit down on this bigger stone and gently let your lower legs and feet dangle in the water ...

The soothing water flows past you; a gentle current lifts your feet, and they start to float. You take a lovely breath in and close your eyes ... with your eyes closed, you can hear the birds singing in the trees. They talk to each other, their perfect voices singing back and forth.

As you sit here absorbing the peace and tranquillity, you can feel the gentle breeze, you can hear the leaves on the trees rustling in the wind, the long grass swaying on the river bank. You smile as you enjoy the wind in your hair and the rippling of the water on your legs and feet ...

Taking a nice deep breath in now ... relaxing, leaning back slightly with the weight of your upper body on your outstretched arms and hands behind you on your stone ... you can feel all your worries, stresses and emotions of the day leaving you as you softly release your breath towards the water ...

Everything that has been concerning you, upsetting you, praying on your mind and giving you sleepless nights is now being washed away downstream ... and as you rest here. You open your eyes to admire this wonderful, soothing place ... now you can see your worries floating away ... little paper boats pass you by, bobbing along, each one carrying your concerns away ... your worries float away on the soothing water ...

Stay here for a moment as you feel the sun on your face, the wind in your hair, enjoying the connection with the water, your connection with the birds, the trees … right now you are completely connected to all the nature around you …

When you are ready to leave this wonderful place of peace and calm, take a lovely deep breath in and carefully stand up on your stepping stone. Turn around, smile and start to head back towards the riverbank …

Collecting your shoes on the way, you head back towards your bike. You follow the path through the trees, listening to the birds, letting the tall grass tickle your fingertips as you walk.

And so, feeling utterly content, you continue on your journey. But now, you take with you the sense of connection and calmness that you found when you were sitting on the stepping stone, admiring the amazing view, taking with you the sense of love and warmth that you absorbed as the sun shone down upon you …

So now, taking a lovely deep breath in, I'd like you to bring your attention back to your surroundings, the place where you were when we started our relaxing journey today …

As you release your breath, start to wiggle your fingers and toes. Rolling your shoulders, … slowly start to open your eyes now, giving them time to focus before you continue with your day.

If you are going to sleep now then simply switch off your phone/tablet and snuggle up under your cosy blanket or duvet.

Thank you for joining us tonight/today, enjoy the rest of your day/sweet dreams.

CHAPTER NINE

Loving you

Chakra healing

A beautifully calming chakra balancing relaxation

Karina Price

Breathing in, breathing out … breathing in, breathing out … when you are ready, relax back and settle down … focus your gaze on an object in the room … a clock, a piece of furniture, anything that feels right for you … so that you don't get distracted by me or anything else … or perhaps you would prefer to close your eyes … whatever you choose to do … will be just right for you … as there isn't a right or wrong way of doing this …

You might like to focus on everything I say … or you might prefer to allow your mind to wander … or maybe you will focus a little and then focus a lot … or perhaps you will simply drift off … but it really doesn't matter whether you hear me or not because in a moment you are going to be the most relaxed you have ever been.

Laying there now … your head resting on the pillow … fully supported … feeling your body connected with the couch underneath you … your entire body being held and supported … supported and held … Now that you are feeling safe and supported, I want you to imagine a golden light above your head … you can feel the comforting, warm, vibrating energy above your body … Imagine this golden light beaming down, through your entire body … down through your head … feeling the warm, golden light relaxing your mind … down through to your neck … your shoulders … instilling calm and comfort as it gently passes down deeper into your body … either side of your spine … relaxing every muscle in your back as it travels down to you hips … massaging your joints and letting any tension dissipate

... Feel the light travel down your thighs, your knees, yours shins ... your body feeling heavier and more relaxed ... this feeling continues down to your ankles ... your feet and each and every toe is feeling relaxed ... ... Your entire being is filled with peace ... love ... comfort ... Feel this magical golden light within you shine brighter ... extending out of your body ... the energy of this light forming a protective bubble of light around you ... feeling calm and relaxed in here ... no worries or tension exist in this golden light ...

Feeling connected to your physical body ... noticing the stillness ... calmness ... acknowledging any areas of discomfort and tension ... becoming aware of whatever is supporting your head ... arms ... back ... legs ... and, in this restful place, begin to imagine a multicoloured orb of light floating in front of you ... vibrating an energy of serenity, balance and well-being ... Use the power of your mind to slowly move the orb closer to you ... trust that the light knows exactly what you need in this moment ... I wonder what it feels like, as its healing light moves to the base of your spine, lighting up your root chakra with a deep red ... feeling a sense of safety and stability ... replacing anxiety with calmness ... Moving up to the area just below your navel, your sacral chakra becomes orange ... releasing all feelings of creativity ... slowly rising up to your solar plexus, mustard yellow illuminates the area below your chest ... notice your confidence and self-esteem increasing ... feel your heart surrounded by green, feeling love for yourself and others ... rising up to your throat now ... a beautiful light blue enables you to calmly speak your truth ... slowly spreading to the centre of your forehead now, indigo ignites your third eye ... believe in yourself ... trust that the answers lay within you ... violet envelops your crown chakra at the top of your head, connecting you with higher consciousness ... and, as you lay here now, you can relax into the feeling of harmony that exists between your physical body, mind and spirit.

Ego-strengthening

Become the more confident, braver, stronger version of you

Maggie Matthews

Now that you are in a state of deep relaxation and calmness, your subconscious mind is opening up and coming to accept all the ideas and statements that are beneficial to you … on a mental, physical and emotional level … to help and guide you to be a more confident, more relaxed, more positive person who can deal with life's everyday drama and problems in a calm, peaceful and relaxed way … where you can feel that you are on top of the world and that nothing can affect you … You have taken control of your life and nobody can demand anything from you or want anything from you unless you decide otherwise … the choice is yours.

You decide because you are a strong and powerful individual … whose confidence radiates out … You have regained your power and it feels good … your whole body lights up with excitement, positivity and happiness … you can feel the love flowing through your body into every muscle, every cell and every nerve ending, feeling yourself be calm, confident, and peaceful.

Your health has improved on every level because you are now this calm, confident person and your self-esteem is soaring … soaring high into the sky like an eagle flying high above the clouds with the air flowing through its wings … feeling free but in control of the destination … just as you are flying high and enjoying your life's journey, which is going to lead you to your desired destination …

You are mentally strong and know what you want and also know what you don't want … you are stronger than you think and can make decisions easily and more confidently ... you are braver than you feel and step outside of your comfort zone to new horizons with confidence and ease ... you no longer feel the fear that used to hold you back from being the person you always wanted to be ... now you are free ... You are fearless and you are worthy ... to be that person and be proud of the reflection that you see in the mirror every day ... you are that person filled with love, hope, acceptance, courage and strength ...

Negative thoughts, negative feelings and negative emotions are a thing of the past ... these are now unacceptable in your life ... they do not control you any more ... for you are the master of your own destiny and the most positive person you know ... you attract only positive people who radiate love ...

You wake up every morning feeling refreshed and eager for another day of success, prosperity and abundance ... Every day just gets better and better ... you go to sleep at night full of gratitude that your day has been productive and prosperous ... you appreciate everything around you that reflects you as a person who loves his/her life as it is filled with beauty ... peace ... and enlightenment ... Beauty shines from within you as well as on the outside. You are in perfect health. You can now accept compliments and say thank you graciously ... You are now a confident, loving, peaceful person that takes life in his/her stride and deals with everyday situations in a calm, relaxed, peaceful, confident way ... As each day passes, you grow from strength to strength, and you are now finally living the life that you have dreamed of.

The heart of the forest

A journey to the heart of the sacred wood, where you encounter love, joy, compassion and wisdom and awaken your loving heart

Jane Hill

Take a moment now, to settle into this blessed time, this beautiful time that you give yourself, here and now …

Spend a few minutes focusing on your breath: breathe in through your nose for four counts and out for eight, in a smooth, easy, unforced way, taking the breath deep into the belly and 'sighing' it out through the mouth …

How often have you longed for time in which to be peaceful and quiet, to be at peace and calm? And now here it is, in this moment …

Take some time now, to accept this quiet and calm time that you have offered yourself – take time to receive it with an open heart and spirit …

Notice the breath, not changing it or judging it, simply noticing it as it comes and goes. And take a moment to accept this time that you have given yourself, to accept it gratefully and wholeheartedly. You may find as you sit, that thoughts, ideas and images come to you, but let them go, let them drift away, just as they have drifted into your mind … …

And so, you find yourself standing at the edge of a great wood. It is a blustery autumn day. The air moves around you, but the trees in the wood are still and quiet.

To get to this wood, you walked across a field and up a gentle slope, which has brought you to the edge of the trees.

What is it that you will see here? What is it that you will do? What will you encounter? As you pause at the edge of the trees, the branches seem to reach out, encouraging you, welcoming you, inviting you to step inside the forest. And so, you do.

You walk in and at once you feel the calm, peaceful atmosphere of this place. Outside the wind is blowing but in here the air is still. Outside the wind is chilly and cool, the autumn air is beginning to make itself known, but inside the wood, although the trees are turning to their autumn colours, the air is mild.

Before you, you see a path leading on through the trees and you step onto the path and follow it. Walking along, you smell the scent of pine in the air, sharp and crisp and fresh. You see the autumn colours of the other trees and a carpet of gold, amber, garnet and ruby spread beneath your feet, the autumn leaves that have fallen. High up above, birds are singing and flying about from one tree to another. Everything here welcomes you and encourages you. You understand that you are safe here, secure, encouraged and known for who you really are ...

Walk on, following the path, feeling delight and joy in your heart, at this beautiful wood welcoming you and sheltering you. How good it is to be here, how peaceful and calm. How often you have longed to find this peace and quiet. Already you begin to feel restored and renewed ...

You walk on, following the path as it twists and turns through the trees, treading on the many, many leaves that have fallen in uncounted years before. The earth is soft beneath your feet, and it is good to walk here ...

There is no need to hurry – it is so calm and beautiful here that it is good to take time to look around and see the beauty of the trees in their autumn glory. And you walk on, following the path, smelling the scent of pine and earth, hearing the birds high up in the treetops ...

As you walk, your curiosity and wonder grow.

Where does this path lead? What will you see? What will you do?

You walk on, knowing that you will find the answers to these questions, trusting and believing that it will become clear why you are here today in this place. And, at that moment, the path takes a bend and brings you out at the edge of a clearing at the heart of the wood ...

You look around with delight; the clearing is carpeted with short grass covered with autumn leaves like beautiful jewels, gleaming and glowing everywhere you look. And of the trees that surround this place, some still wear their autumn leaves and some are pine trees and are dark green. How good it is to be here, in this fair place!

Everything here is quite still and peaceful and, all at once, you know that here you will find your true self, you are your true self. This beautiful clearing at the heart of the wood allows you to know and acknowledge your true nature. This is the place to come to when you wish to know and nourish your heart. And you understand that, although you have never been here before, everything here in this place knows you, recognises you and acknowledges who you truly are …

Look more closely around the clearing now; at its centre stands a great hawthorn tree. Many of its leaves have fallen and lie around it but it still wears some golden, amber and copper leaves and ruby berries on its branches and twigs.

You cross the clearing, walking over the springy, carpeted grass to stand beneath the tree and spend some time gazing up into its branches, which spread over you, sheltering and protecting you. You realise that here you are safe and known …

As you understand this, the hawthorn's leaves and twigs rustle, acknowledging you and your true self and, at once, in a moment, you see yourself as this place sees you. In a moment of joy, your true self is revealed to you.

You are a living, shining being of golden light. You understand that your purpose in coming here is to know this, to acknowledge it and to live it …

You are a living being of light …

You understand that you are compassionate, loving, wise, joyful, healing and healed …

Take some time to know yourself as a being of golden light, standing beneath the golden hawthorn tree at the heart of the golden clearing, at the heart of the shining wood … …

This is a place of great and deep power, you are a being of great and deep, subtle power.

Take a moment to sit with your awareness of this deep power within you …

Here, now, you can acknowledge your vast potential, unlimited, unbounded, for compassion, for wisdom, for joy, for healing and for love. Your true nature, your true human nature is this. You are far more powerful than you allow yourself to know or to be. Take some moments to sit with this new understanding of your humanity and spirit …

And understand that to come here to this beautiful, healing, powerful place, to encounter this, to acknowledge this new understanding, is part of your practice of understanding your true self and your true nature …

Sit for a few more moments with this strong awareness. For this moment, for now, feel your powerful but gentle energy spreading out all around you, unlimited, unbounded … …

This gentle, powerful energy is free, free to stream out of you to go wherever it wishes to go, to lead wherever it wishes to take you. To encourage you to be your true self. In this moment, in this now, you sit at the centre of a vast sea of peaceful energy, calm power that has no limit, that has no end … …

This is the true nature of our reality, the true nature of the cosmos, the world. Loving, peaceful, calm energy and power. And for today and for this moment, you are connected with it, at the heart and centre of it. You are as one with it. Take some moments to sit with this awareness. Take as long as you like … …

In this moment, you are changed forever. With this new awareness of your true nature, your life is changed from now on. This new awareness, new understanding is awoken in your loving, compassionate, wise, healing and healed heart forever. Here, at the heart of the forest, your heart, your spirit, your soul is awakened forever. Your life is changed. Although you will return to the outer world, your heart will always remember and return to this place, the heart of the forest.

At last, at last, you have found this place and its many blessings, and your heart, your spirit, your soul is calm and peaceful, healed and renewed …

Take time to savour this moment and to accept it gratefully, humbly, joyfully. Sit with your new awareness of your capacity for love, joy, wisdom, compassion, knowing that your heart shines within you with these new gifts. They were always within your heart, but now they are awakened and will stay with you … …

Now it is time to look around the clearing, and to see once again all of the gem-like colours of autumn around you. The trees are still and peaceful, as you are. You understand deeply now that the truest, most authentic and real power lies in stillness, calm and peace.

You gaze up into the branches of the great hawthorn tree spread over you and thank it for protecting and sheltering you in your visit here. The tree rustles and quivers, acknowledging your thanks and new understanding.

Take time to thank the whole clearing, the whole place for showing and giving you this knowledge, helping you to understand the deep, subtle reality, the deep, subtle knowledge at the heart of all things. Now you know that you are indeed a being of golden light, peace, compassion, joy, love, wisdom and healing. This is your truth and your reality. It can't be otherwise ...

Take a last look around the clearing and then walk back across the grass, back to the trees and the path by which we came. There you can turn and look around again, knowing that you can come back here whenever you wish to and you will find this place waiting for us. In any season at any time of year this place, sacred and blessed, always waits for you to visit once again.

But, for now, turn and walk away back along the path by which you came. Walk through the wood; as you pass the trees, they rustle and quiver, acknowledging you and your new understanding about yourself.

Know that you are changed from this day forward, everything is different from now on ...

Follow the path, passing the rustling trees and, as you go, notice that you are light-hearted and joyful, having this new understanding. Walk on, following the path as it twists and turns through the trees, taking delight in the scent of pine in the air around you, the mildness of the air, the autumn leaves spread out like a carpet, the springiness and softness of the ground. Feel the peace and calm of this blessed wood in your heart ...

You walk on and come to the edge of the wood. Take a moment to thank the wood for everything it has done for you and shown you. Know that you can come back to this wood at any time, and it will always be waiting for you as will everything in it that you wish to see. But, for now, with a last thanks and farewell, step out of the wood and walk down the gentle slope away from it, knowing that you will return here at a future time, whenever you need to do so. You can come back here at any time, and you will find the forest and the clearing, everything within it, waiting for you once again.

And so, having visited the sacred wood, take some moments to notice the breath, not trying to change it or judge it, simply noticing it ...

Return to your everyday world with the blessing of the sacred wood and the hawthorn tree. Remember always the new understanding that you now have and, whenever you need to, recall the sacred hawthorn tree at the heart of the clearing, at the heart of the wood.

The paper boat

For someone who is helping others to the detriment of themselves

Tania Taylor

Really allow yourself to enjoy these precious moments all for you now …
and I'd like you to imagine something for me … I'd like you to imagine that
it is dawn, the sun is just rising in the sky … and you find yourself standing
in front of the prettiest of waterfalls … Not too close, just a nice distance
from which you can thoroughly enjoy watching the water as it falls into the
tranquil stream below …

You take a few moments to consider how far this water has travelled …
Where was it in the world when it fell from the clouds in the sky as tiny
droplets of rain that then led it to be right here in front of you? … Where
will it travel after this?

How many people might bask in the coolness of the water before it
reaches the ocean? Will it reach the ocean at all? And, if so, how long will it
take for it to get there?

You find yourself mesmerised by the flow of the water, the beautiful
sounds as the water rushes down into the stream in front of you, and you
feel so comfortable … so comfortable in fact that you choose to get a blanket
out of your bag and sit down by the water's edge, carefully watching as the
water falls down through the waterfall and moves into the gentle stream
next to you.

Beside you, you can see the morning dew on the grassy bank of the water's edge, individual droplets of fresh water; occasionally a droplet will just gently move down the blade of grass to the ground below.

Your attention is brought back to the waterfall again and you notice the occasional bubble created by the water hitting the surface of the stream at such speed, and you watch as those bubbles slowly drift past you where you lie, and down through the stream … And this gives you an idea …

You look inside your bag and find some paper … You're going to make a spectacular paper boat today … and you're not sure quite how you know this, but because you've had the idea, you just know that you can make it happen … and so, you find yourself folding your paper until eventually you have created the most incredible paper boat …

You admire your workmanship, one simple idea, turned into reality just by you having confidence that you could make this little dream become a reality for you …

You have some coloured wax crayons in your bag … and before you know it your little paper boat is looking spectacular … And the wax has helped to create a waterproof barrier too …

So now the time has come to put your little plan into action. You move over to the water's edge and place your paper boat upon the water … You feel so proud of yourself and your workmanship as your boat floats perfectly within the slow-moving flow …

And you choose to follow your sailboat now, so you gather up your things and place them back into your bag, and carefully and steadily walk beside your wonderful paper boat …

The boat travels at a slow but exhilarating pace, sometimes it takes a little bit longer as it's met with boulders and rocks jutting out from the bottom of the stream; this gives you time, as you follow the worn path on the grassy bank beside this beautiful water …

There are times when the boat finds itself travelling a little faster as it floats down mini waterfalls created by yet more rocks and boulders jutting out from the water below … Occasionally, it almost stops completely as it finds itself blocked by a fallen tree branch … but the flow of water helps, and you watch as your paper boat overcomes any obstacles that it finds in its way …

You have been strolling slowly alongside your boat when you notice a frog up ahead … It's a friendly looking fellow and you can see it admiring your boat … The frog explains that he is trying to get to a point much further downstream, but he has injured his leg … He asks if he can have a lift in your boat ... "Of course," you say ... And so, the frog hops onto your little boat and you continue to follow it down the winding stream, passing round barriers and boulders that crop up every now and again, flowing quickly down the dips that occur and creating tiny waterfalls in their wake ...

As you continue, you notice a caterpillar ... it reminds you of the famous book about the caterpillar that was very hungry ... She lifts her head up as she sees your boat and she asks you if she can ride your boat too ... "I was picked up by a small child and moved up stream away from my family; they are too far away for me to get back to them, please may I join the boat ride too?" ... You carefully consider your response ...

The frog needed your help, and you were happy to help, you knew your paper boat could take the weight of the young frog, and now the caterpillar needs your help too, you're certain with the caterpillar being so small and light all will be just fine, and so you agree, and the caterpillar jumps aboard to go and find her family too ...

As you all continue, you find that the water's edge is becoming a little tricky to walk along and you're slowed down by a few brambles in your path ... But then you notice the blackberries and you take a little pot out of your bag to collect some in and save for later ... You know they are a perfect snack for whenever you may need them ...

As you catch back up to your little boat and the frog and the caterpillar, you are drawn to the noise of the trickling stream, the subtle sounds of nature, and as you pinpoint the individual noises, you notice the noise of a cricket ...

The stream has come to a very slow little pool of water created by half a dam of rocks that a small child must have built ... And there upon a rock is the cricket ...

The cricket admires your boat and explains he wants to reach a place further downstream and hopes he might use your boat to assist ... "Of course," you say, "hop on board," and the cricket joins the caterpillar and the frog and all of you continue your journey downstream ...

The frog tells you that his sore leg happened as he got it trapped between a rock and a hard place ... the caterpillar explained that she was quite happy being played with by the young child but, when she realised she had been taken from her home and her family, she felt all hope was lost as she tried and failed to make her way back ... The cricket tells you about how he is now an old man and getting from 'a' to 'b' isn't quite as simple as it always had been ...

You are happy to help but you are a little worried about your boat; it has been travelling a long time and it is only made of paper, it already has three guests on top of it, and it looks like it might be beginning to give way under the surface … but it is plodding along just as it always had from the beginning and so you continue feeling pleased that you are helping so many others …

The frog and the caterpillar and the cricket all begin talking about how hungry they are, and you explain that you picked some blackberries earlier … You give them all of your blackberries and they are so happy to receive the fruits of your labour …

The sun is now high in the sky, and you feel its rays touching your skin. The frog, the caterpillar and the cricket say how easily they get sunburnt, and you explain you have a wonderful solution, and you give them all of your sun cream too. They are all so grateful.

Your little paper boat is continuing to bob along merrily, gently down the stream, when you notice a magnificent dragonfly on a rock up ahead … wow is she beautiful …

As you get closer, you can hear she is wheezing and out of breath … She explains that she has asthma and doesn't have her medicine with her, but she could get to it a little further downstream if she could have a lift on your beautiful boat …

And, before you know it, you now have four guests on your little boat … On the surface, everything appears fine, but underneath the surface, the little boat is beginning to deteriorate …

"Just a little bit further, little boat," you coax, as the boat continues to hold its four passengers for a little longer still …

Eventually, though, the boat can go no further, and it is time for the passengers to get off …

The frog, the caterpillar, the cricket and the dragonfly are all so happy that they have managed to reach their destination. It fills you with joy and you wave goodbye to all of them as you turn and make your way back up stream …

The sun is already beginning to sink lower now, and you realise that you have not had an opportunity to use your sun cream, and you haven't eaten, as you gave all of your blackberries away … Your feet are aching now as you had wanted to ensure your new friends got to their destinations … And you began to feel really tired …

You trudge back through the brambles, receiving a few scrapes and scratches along the way ... and you manage to find a couple of blackberries that hadn't been picked, so you give yourself a little more energy for the journey back ...

And, eventually, you find yourself back at the beautiful waterfall ... Only now it looks even more spectacular as the sun creates rainbows throughout the misty spray surrounding the falling water ...

You lie down on your blanket, feeling an overwhelming sense of tiredness, and you reflect on your long day ... You consider how you would have felt if you hadn't helped the frog, the caterpillar, the cricket, and the dragonfly ...

You know you wouldn't have walked for as long; you wouldn't be feeling so achy or sunburnt and hungry either ... And yet you couldn't 'NOT' have helped them ...

And you consider what you could have done instead to help them to help themselves ... You had noticed many leaves floating on the water's surface ... even a lily pad at one point that created shade from the sun ... All would have been more than substantial for your new friends to have made their way downstream ...

And you consider what if your friends found themselves needing a lift once again ... would they know they could use a leaf or a lily pad in the future? ... Or would they be stranded, hoping you and your paper boat will show up again and come to their rescue?

And you consider your motivation for helping people in the future ... It is always a wonderful feeling to help others, but you recognise that today you were helping others in a way that was detrimental to yourself ... You were helping others in a way that did not enable them to grow and to flourish and to learn how they could help themselves in the future ...

As you stare back into that beautiful waterfall, you once again become mesmerised by the incredible flow and the sounds of the water ... and you feel good ... because you now know what to do the next time someone needs your help ... you know that life often has challenges and that some of them feel more challenging than others ... but you also know that if you take on everyone else's challenges ... you leave them reliant on you, and you leave yourself feeling unwell ...

So, you vow now to continue to help others when the time is right, but to always take care of you, for you are a priority too.

Using gratitude for inner peace

A guided visualisation which stimulates the senses and encourages gratitude and self-contentment

Anne Gregory

Allow yourself a lovely, deep breath in … and relax … as you breathe out …

Adjust your position if you need to … and inhale deeply …

Pause for a second, hold that breath and then breathe out slowly and steadily … and relax …

Can you feel your body and mind relaxing? … …

Breathe in again, long and slow … pause … and exhale …

Allow your eyes to close if you wish … and connect with the present moment … …

In your mind's eye … picture the things that are around you …

Let your mind appreciate the physical items that surround you …

As you think about each item … picture it … savour it … and then move on to the next one … …

Take your time … …

Really appreciate everything you have around you … …

Continue to do this until you have mentally scanned your surroundings in your mind … …

Now bring your thoughts to what you can feel … …

Perhaps you can feel your feet on the floor if you are sitting down at the moment …

Maybe you can feel the weight of your body sinking into the chair or the sofa or the bed you are on …

Give yourself permission to relax even further ... notice the feeling ... observe it ... and relax completely ... ...

You may not yet realise just how peaceful you feel ... ...

A person could (name) learn how to feel calmer and more composed simply by thinking about it ...

Now bring your attention to any sounds you can hear ... either around you or in the distance ... ...

What can you hear? ... Identify the sound ... then let it go ... and relax ... ...

Now focus your attention on all the things in your life you are grateful for ... ...

Think about the people in your life that you appreciate ... perhaps your family ... your friends ... your work colleagues ...

And as you bring each one to mind ... think of a positive interaction you have had with them ... ...

How does that make you feel? ... Joyful? ... Happy? ... Perhaps it makes you smile ... ...

You probably already know that laughter is the best medicine ... it is so good for you ... so do not delay ...

Think about the activities you enjoy doing ... ...

What brings you joy in your life? ... The work you do? ... The hobbies you take part in? ... Spending time with your pets? ... Your garden? ...

As you bring these activities to mind ... allow yourself to feel the positivity they bring ... ...

Feel the positivity flow through you and absorb those pleasant thoughts and feelings and visualisations ... ...

Can you see things more clearly now? ... You can learn to associate that clarity and certainty with calmness and confidence ...

Know that you can tap back into those thoughts and feelings and visualisations whenever you want to ... ...

Can you imagine how good it will feel when you can just let go and notice that you can do this even more easily? ...

And bring back those wonderful images and sensations whenever you need to ...

Give yourself permission to live your life ... from this moment onwards with grace and gratitude ... with courage and confidence ...

Connect with your inner creativity ...

Commit to living your life to the fullest ... because you deserve it ...

Sooner or later you will fully appreciate how much better things are ... all down to you ...

Trust your inner voice ... it knows you the best ... and it always has your best interests at heart ... ...

When you trust your instincts, you know you are on the right track ... as your instincts will not let you down ...

Would you like to trust your inner voice slowly or quickly? ... ...

You do not need to look any further ... simply recognise your own needs ... and remember that it is okay to help yourself ...

Be aware of ... and grateful for ... all the strengths you have ... whatever they may be ... ...

Your kindness ... your compassion ... your patience ... your positivity ... as you continue to look for the joy in anything and everything you see and do ...

What happens when you really think about how successful you have been? ... ...

In so many areas of your life ... your previous success can inspire you to reach even greater heights ... reaching higher and higher and higher ... ...

You may not know if you are going to enjoy something until you try it ... ...

I know that will not stop you from trying lots of new things in your future ... because you may find something that makes you feel wonderful, and you may learn something new ... to add to all of the other things you have already learned ... ...

You can allow yourself to feel confident in whatever you choose to do ... knowing that it can bring you joy ... knowing that you are fully in tune with yourself ... your surroundings ... nature ... the world ... the universe ...

Allow your self-worth to ground you ... your self-belief to grow stronger ... and your confidence to expand within you ... knowing that you can deal with anything in a calm ... balanced way ... ...

Wonders of the galaxy

Welcome to a world of kindness, where you can do everything you were previously fearful of achieving

Karina Price

Lying in the middle of the moonlit desert, you stare up to the night sky and admire the stars before you. Galaxies beyond galaxies … magic is everywhere you look … and, as you gaze up, you notice that you're feeling lighter and lighter … In a moment, I am going to count up from one to ten and, with each number, you will feel more and more relaxed and anything that is weighing you down just doesn't seem to weigh you down any more.

One … feeling relaxed, the silk blanket underneath you begins to float you up higher and higher.

Two … as you float on up, you notice that anything that would usually weigh you down just doesn't seem to bother you any more.

Three … worries, tension, stress just seems to slip away … away from your body … away from your mind. Because where you're going, nothing can weigh you down.

Four … feeling lighter, calmer, and more in control as you float on up to …

Five … feeling more confident and noticing the positive changes within you now.

Six … floating up above the trees … lighter and lighter …

Seven … calmer and full of peace.

Eight … calmer still.

Nine … blissfully floating through the clouds …

Ten ... floating peacefully up into space ... the moon's white, golden beam shining down onto you now.

You are at one with the wonders of the universe, connected in every way, with stars, with the solar system. Everything that you can see, you are connected to in mind, body and spirit. And this means that you no longer have anything to fear. Because you are everything. You are happiness ... you are confident ... anything is possible here ... you are everything that you need to be here and now.

Float towards a beautiful galaxy of brightly coloured planets and stars. And then you float on down to a wonderful planet that you're drawn to that just seems to feel right for you. As you land, you land into a world of safety. In fact, it's so safe on this planet that your mind starts to wonder what it would be like to do anything because you no longer have any fears; you start to wonder what you would do if all your worries just seem to disappear. Who would you choose to talk to right now, what would you choose to do, what would you choose to let go of, if you knew that you were in a world of safety? A world of kindness? And just let go of the need to be in control because here you don't need to be. Release that hurt now because anything that happens will happen just in the right time for you.

You start to become tired now, and you just can't seem to keep your eyes open ... your eyes are feeling heavy ... heavy now ... and you begin to drift and dream ... dream and drift ...

Woodland spa

Find an array of positive affirmations to help personal growth
in this beautiful woodland meadow

Karina Price

… and you find yourself walking through a peaceful meadow, flowers swaying beautifully in a soft, warm breeze … noticing the sounds around you … the sounds of the birds, grass dancing in the wind, peacefully … feeling the soft, warm grass beneath your feet … deeply relaxed and connected to the earth beneath you. In this moment, a deep feeling of calm surrounds and immerses you … and, as you continue to walk through this meadow of contentment, you start to feel lighter and lighter … and gently begin to float above the meadow … floating like a soft cloud without a care in the world … peacefully noticing the blue sky before you … feeling safe and deeply relaxed, you float towards a beautiful forest …

And you gently ground yourself in a place that feels right for you. Tall, wise trees surround you and autumn colours serenade you … orange, brown, yellow and green … and perhaps this is a good moment to imagine the air around you is a wonderful colour that reminds you of every positive feeling or thought you've ever had … I wonder what colour that would be? And, with each breath you take … see it filling your body … hear it filling your mind with positive and confident thoughts and feelings … that's right, the colour is spreading all around now, as you begin to remember those positive thoughts and all the things you are good at … so keep breathing in this confident, positive colour that reminds you of your strengths and positive resources and let it spread all around you now.

Now look a little more closely ... can you notice any other areas that have a different colour? The colour of any possible tension ... or the colour of self-doubt, perhaps? I wonder what colour that would be ... well, if there are any ... begin to breathe those colours out of your body ... right out of your mind, breathe out that tension ... breathe out that self-doubt, and breathe in that wonderful, happy, confident feeling ... and let it spread all around your body and mind ... that's right, brilliant ... and in this comfortable, slightly dreamy state, perhaps you can bring your attention back to the beautiful forest that surrounds you ...

Notice the sounds of nature ... the trees, leaves chasing each other in the mild breeze ... the smell of pine trees and fresh grass. Standing now, take a moment to ground with the earth beneath you ... imagine roots from your body connecting with the earth and growing deeper and deeper ... feeling connected to the forest ... as one ... giving you a deep sense of wisdom, courage and strength ... and your mind reminds you of what you need to hear right now ... I AM DIVINE, I AM AT PEACE, I SEE CLEARLY, I HEAR AND SPEAK MY TRUTH, I AM AN EXPRESSION OF LOVE, I AM WORTHY OF LOVE, I FORGIVE MYSELF AND OTHERS, I FOLLOW THE VOICE OF MY HEART, MY POTENTIAL IS UNLIMITED, I ACT WITH COURAGE, I AM CONNECTED WITH NATURE.

In the distance, you can hear a stream, clear water calmly making its way through the forest ... make your way towards the stream, feeling a deep sense of relaxation with every step you take. In this moment, you notice a deer contentedly enjoying its environment ... and a butterfly happily flutters past you ...

... and now you find yourself beside a lake, the sun's rays lazily settled on the surface ... and, as you sit there, you notice a young child throwing pebbles into the lake and a pebble skips along the surface ... once ... twice ... three times ... before it slowly starts to sink into the lake ... deeper and deeper ... and, as the pebble floats on down ... you notice deeper and deeper feelings of relaxation ... sitting there with your eyes closed ... noticing the warm sun on your face.

Now the sun slowly settles down behind the horizon ... perhaps this is the perfect time to find a safe place next to the edge of the still lake. Feeling calm and relaxed, you notice the moon gently making its way into the purple night sky, surrounded and supported by the magical stars. You notice the reflection of the moon on the lake before you ... ripples of beautiful moonlight … this is your time to look at the stars and make a wish upon a shooting star … trust that whatever your heart desires will come true … you are confident, powerful and the magic of nature lies within you … you are strong and capable of achieving any goals you set your mind to … and your mind starts to wander and drift off into a parallel universe … here you are your ultimate best self … happy … confident … and you truly believe in yourself and your capabilities.

And in this peacefully dreamy state … you start to drift off … feeling sleepy now, your mind guides you to an incredibly calm and relaxing spa … a spa for your mind and body. Feeling deeply relaxed now, in a wonderfully luxurious woodland cabin spa … peaceful harp music and healing sound bowls playing in the near distance … feeling the warmth of a woodburning fire … golden yellows, deep reds and burnt orange flames warm your skin to a temperature that feels just right for you … scented candles flickering on the mantlepiece … and salt lamps of different sizes and colours peacefully placed … as you lay here now, the sound of the rain captures your attention … raindrops lazily making their way down the window … feeling deeply comforted by this sound … relaxed … at ease … and safe … the rain washing away any worries, tension or anxiety … cleansing your mind, body and soul. In between the sounds … sounds of the rain … music … crackling fire … you notice the silence in between the sounds … … the silence … the stillness … the emptiness in between the sounds … any thoughts just seem to float away into the silence … and any thoughts that remain in this moment are welcome … welcome to stay for a moment … or welcome to float off to a place of peace … feel this sense of silence and stillness now … feel this peaceful feeling in and around your body … that's right … your mind knows exactly how to achieve this wonderfully peaceful and calm state of well-being … …

And now you find yourself comfortably resting on a soft couch … feeling lazy … ready for a massage of your choice … settle down … breathing in, breathing out, breathing in, breathing out. You can smell the lavender and eucalyptus aromatherapy oils … helping your mind to settle and your body to relax … feeling really calm … deeply relaxed … a beautiful rose quartz massage roller blissfully gliding up and down your back … up and down … up and down … smooth, gentle rolls of contentment making its way up to your shoulders … loosening any tension … easing any stiffness in your neck … any pains gently lessening … massaging your head … the top of your scalp ... deeply relaxing every pressure point ... your body feeling heavier ... sinking into the couch ... I wonder which arm feels heavier ... perhaps it's your left arm ... or maybe it's your right ... I wonder which leg feels heavier ... but it really doesn't matter if it's your left or your right ...

And, as you lie here now, all your worries just seem to float away and slowly disappear ... you don't need to be anywhere, do anything, nobody wanting or needing your attention ... this moment is completely free ... hassle free ... stress free ... and, as you lie here now, perhaps you can allow your mind to imagine happy, positive memories ... things that make you feel good, things that you have achieved, perhaps as a child or more recently ... something that you are good at ... maybe you're a kind friend or family member ... perhaps you are good at coping with challenges ... or maybe you have a creative imagination ... your mind knows exactly how good you are ... so take your time ... no need to rush or hurry ... simply go to that happy place in your mind now ... how does it feel ... what can you see ... hear ... make those sounds louder, colours brighter ... perhaps there are areas of this happy place in your mind that are hidden away, behind shadows ... go to that place now and turn on the light switch ... warm, golden light exposing your hidden strengths ... perhaps you can now remember things that you were good at all along but forgot they were there ... I wonder what these are ... YOU ARE CONFIDENT, YOU ARE STRONG, YOU CAN DO ANYTHING YOU PUT YOUR MIND TO, YOU ARE RESILIENT, YOU ARE VALUED, YOU DESERVE TO BE HAPPY ... and know that whenever you need to feel happy you can return to this happy place in your mind whenever you need to.

Imagine what life would be like in the parallel universe ... what are you doing ... who are you with ... where do you live ... work ... what are you doing for fun ...

CHAPTER TEN

Past life regression

Past life regression

Jeff Lloyd

Make sure that you're sitting or lying comfortably, uncross your legs and your arms, just take a few moments to get comfortable and, when you're settled, take in a couple of deep breaths, letting out all the stresses and tensions of the day. Begin to relax at a pace that's right for you, and as you follow my instructions, you'll find that you'll enter a deep relaxation, remembering that wherever you travel to or whatever place you find yourself in, you are safe and always in control.

As you begin to let go and relax, just allow your eyes to gently close, that's right, really relax those eyelids, just let them melt and stick together. Relax them so much until you feel unable to open them and, as you do so, let all the muscles around your eyes relax and all the muscles on your face, the muscles around your mouth, and your cheeks … … that's right and just let them all relax. Focus now on your forehead; that's where we keep a lot of tension and all our thoughts and all our worries, so just let those muscles relax too, allow those thoughts and worries just to drift away. As you do so, let that relaxation run down your face, down your neck and your throat, all the way down to your shoulders and, as you continue to relax, allow that relaxation to run down both arms, all the way down to your fingers, so that both arms become loose and heavy. Now, again focus on your breathing and just let any background noises or distractions take you deeper and deeper and allow that relaxation to flow around your stomach, your upper and lower back, down to both legs, all the way down to your feet, so that you are totally relaxed.

Now that you feel relaxed, I want you to visualise a wonderful golden light just above you and allow this glowing, healing and protecting light to slowly descend and encompass your whole body making you feel safe and warm. Now you're in this safe protected space, I'd like you to imagine yourself walking through a beautiful, warm, sunlit garden, a special garden, in fact a secret garden, which only you have access to. As you walk, you notice how lovely and green and neat the lawns are kept, which, in turn, are surrounded by well-kept borders of flowers displaying their magnificent array of colours, such as the highly scented red and yellow roses, which you can smell as you pass them by. As you walk further, you can feel a gentle, warm breeze upon your face, as you hear the bird song in the background, interrupted only by the occasional busy bee going about his work, collecting nectar from the brightly coloured flowers in the border.

After a while, you come across a small bench, which you decide to sit upon and take in the full view of the garden, enjoying the feel of the gentle warmth of the sun's rays upon your face. As you look around the garden, you notice a large fountain and listen to the gentle flow of water and watch as all the colours of the rainbow are caught in each droplet of water. As you enjoy the experience of the all-encompassing sights and sounds of the garden, you notice some white steps in the corner that draw your attention as you wonder where they could lead to. Your curiosity finally gets the better of you and you decide to go over and have a look.

As you approach them, you notice a small, neatly written sign by the side of the steps, which says, "Let these ten steps lead you back through the ages and to other lifetimes." Now, not only are you curious and intrigued, but excited, and you decide to slowly walk down the ten steps to see what you will discover, which, to help you, I will now count you down as you go and explore one of your past lives, remembering that you are perfectly safe and in control.

So let us take those steps now … ten … going down, nine … deeper and deeper, eight … seven … so relaxed now, six … drifting down and down, five … the more you relax, the deeper you can go, the deeper you go the more you relax, four … three … getting closer and closer, two … to another life, one … and, as you take the last step, you find you are in a different place and lifetime!

Describe what you can see … …

A note from the editor

If you have found use upon these pages, please help my small business out by leaving feedback here: https://bit.ly/3OTMHys and leaving a review on Amazon.

As a solo entrepreneur the time you take out of your day to leave a positive review means the absolute world to me, and I promise I read every piece of feedback left.

If you would like to read other books written by me and be informed when more books are released, please visit https://amzn.to/3PTC9A6 and select "Follow author".

Thank you.

Much love,

Tania
xoxo